W & 6   30

C[ontents]

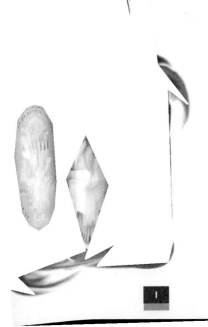

Author: Jeff Evans

Published by CAMRA Books, Campaign for Real Ale, 230 Hatfield Road, St Albans AL1 4LW
Tel: (01727) 867201 Fax: (01727) 867670
Managing Editor: Mark Webb
Design and layout: McKie Associates
Cover photography: Profile Photography

ISBN 1-85249-128-0

Cover: Gale's Prize Old Ale (page 69), Fuller's 1845 (page 67), Shepherd Neame Spitfire (page155), Marston's Oyster Stout (page109).

First Edition, August 1997

Great effort has gone into researching the contents of this book, but no responsibility can be taken for errors.

Introduction

In 1987, the Campaign for Real Ale's *Good Beer Guide* made one of its more pes-
simistic and, thankfully, less successful predictions. In a feature on bottled beers it
claimed that 'by the end of the century Britain's remaining breweries will produce
between them no more than a dozen bottled beers'. But look around you as you visit
your local off-licence or supermarket. Far from having only a dozen beers under glass
as we head towards the Millennium, we have never been so blessed with bottles. The
majority contain foreign lagers or brewery processed ales but an increasing number
now offer beer which is naturally conditioned in the bottle – in other words, real ale.
And that's where this new guide comes in.

For a number of years the CAMRA *Good Beer Guide* has listed which bottle-conditioned beers are brewed by Britain's breweries, but, apart from a stark mention of
the original gravities and alcohol by volume figures, that's all the *Good Beer Guide* – with
its focus, justifiably, in cask real ale and the pubs which sell it – has had room to provide. *The CAMRA Guide to Real Ale in a Bottle* is intended as a companion book to the
Good Beer Guide, filling the void in coverage of the bottled real ale scene. Five or six
years ago, the fact that this book didn't exist was a matter of little concern. There were,
after all, a mere handful of bottle-conditioned beers available in the UK. Now all that
has changed and the publication of such a book is more than overdue.

What Is Real Ale?

Real ale, according to the CAMRA-agreed description in the *Oxford English Dictionary*,
is 'beer which has been brewed and stored in the traditional way, and which has undergone secondary fermentation of the yeast in the container from which it is dispensed'.
In other words, it is unfiltered, unpasteurised, uncarbonated beer which matures up to
the point at which it is drunk. Close inspection of the *OED* definition reveals that dis-
cussion centres purely on draught beer, but, as bottled beer can also fit the prescribed
characteristics, it is fair to say that bottle-conditioned beers – beers which contain yeast
and enjoy a secondary fermentation in the bottle, as opposed to the pasteurised, filtered and carbonated variety – are real ales, too. Indeed, that is a view CAMRA has
propagated all along. So, when searching for a real ale in a bottle, look for the presence of yeast. This can usually be seen in the form of a sticky or silty sediment at the
bottom of the bottle, but it can become loose, particularly if the beer is not poured
carefully. Not that the sediment will harm you (the accepted theory is that it just might
make you more 'regular'), but it can make the beer a bit, well, yeasty, and possibly a
bit more chewy, although the greatest disadvantage is that it makes the beer less
appealing to the eye.

How Bottle-Conditioned Beers Are Brewed

Before we involve ourselves with how the yeast gets into the bottle, we need to consider how the beer itself is produced. All beer begins with malted barley. This is barley grain which has been partially germinated to help release vital sugars needed for the brewing process and then kilned to prevent further germination. The degree of kilning also dictates the character of the malt; the more 'baked' the malt, the darker the colour and the roastier the taste. Some are toasted black for bitter, coffeeish flavours; others are merely lightly crisped for a sweeter or nuttier taste. At the brewery the malt is crushed and then combined in a vessel called a mash tun with hot water (known as liquor in the trade). This liquor has usually been treated to remove unsuitable chemicals or to emulate the natural brewing waters of towns like Burton upon Trent.

After an hour and a half's mashing and stirring, a thick, sweet liquid called wort is formed. This is then run off from the mash tun and diverted into a boiler known as a copper, leaving behind the spent grain, which is sprayed – or 'sparged' – to extract any last sugars and then sold for animal fodder. In the copper, the wort is boiled up with hops which add bitterness and sometimes herby, spicy or floral characters. Like malts, hops come in many varieties. Some are very bitter; others milder. Some make themselves known in the aroma; others are expressed in the taste. Hops also act as a preservative. They can be added as whole hop flowers or as compressed pellets. Some brewers use hop oils (concentrated hop extract), but it is widely considered that such oils can be too astringent. The hops are added at various stages of the boil, some times 'adjuncts' are introduced. These include sugars, which add to the fermentability of the wort, and maize, which helps produce a good head on the finished beer, but such additives (and other less wholesome ingredients) are always hotly opposed by purists.

After an hour or two in the copper, the hops are strained out and the hopped wort is run off and cooled. When the temperature has dipped sufficiently, the wort is pumped into a fermenting vessel, yeast is added ('pitched' is the technical term) and fermentation begins. Yeast is a single-celled fungus whose value to the brewer lies in its ability to turn the sugars in the wort into alcohol and carbon dioxide (which gives beer its natural effervescence). Each yeast, however, also has its own character which is skilfully harnessed and preserved by brewery chemists. Many breweries use the same yeasts for decades, ensuring that the brewery maintains its own style and individuality. The yeast is re-processed and re-used after each brew, with any excess generated sold to companies like Marmite.

During the first few days of fermentation, the yeast works furiously with the wort, growing quickly and covering the wort with a thick, undulating duvet of foam. Most is skimmed off, but some sinks into the brew and continues to work, eating up the sugars and generating more carbon dioxide and alcohol. A few days later, this 'primary fermentation' is deemed over and bottle-conditioned beers and other, 'processed' bottled beers go their separate ways.

Processed, or 'bright', beers are chilled, filtered and pasteurised, effectively killing off and removing any living yeast still in the brew. They are then carbonated and put into bottles. Some 'brewery-conditioned' beers are given time at the brewery to mature. Indeed some classic bottled beers are not bottle-conditioned at all, but are brought to maturity at the brewery before bottling. These include Courage Bulldog and Guinness Foreign Extra Stout. Other beers follow a halfway-house system whereby the beer is sterile filtered to remove the yeast, but is not pasteurised. They strictly speaking do not condition in the bottle but do have a fresher taste than pasteurised beers. Lees Harvest Ale is one example.

For bottle-conditioned beers, however, the next stage varies from brewery to brewery. Some breweries adopt the simplest form of bottle-conditioning. They just syphon the beer from the cask into the bottle, yeast and all. This can be a rather hit and miss affair, as not enough yeast may get into the bottle to ensure a good secondary fermentation and the beer may be rather flat when opened. Other breweries take greater pains to ensure their beers have just the right level of fizz. They fine or filter out the tired old yeast and replace it with fresh yeast, which may be a special strain which works well in bottles. The technically precise will check the yeast count under the microscope to guarantee that the right amount of yeast is present. Some kräusen the beer for bottling. This involves adding an amount of partially fermented wort to the beer to give the yeast new sugars to react with and so generate more life. Others prime the beer, using sugar solutions which again provide the yeast with something new to feed on. Once capped, bottles are often warm-conditioned at the brewery for a few weeks, to ensure the secondary fermentation gets off to a good start, and are then shipped out to the trade.

Those are the bare bones of beer brewing. Each brewery, of course, has its own subtly different methods and uses recipes which combine various types of malts with various types of hops, in greater or lesser quantities. By varying brewing temperatures and conditioning times, and by introducing the ingredients at various stages, they contrive to produce, collectively, a magnificent array of flavours. Even brews using exactly the same base ingredients can taste dramatically different. It's one of the pleasures of beer drinking.

Bottled Beer: An Historical View

Though glass blowing is an ancient skill, commercial production of bottled beers in any form only stems from the middle of the 19th century. The Egyptians may well have used glass bottles as long ago as 1400 BC, and some brewers, it seems, began to appreciate the value of the bottle in keeping and even improving beer at some time during the 16th century, but practical manufacture of glass, particularly in bottle form, had to wait until the Industrial Revolution.

Glass as a container took a major leap forward in 1821, when a Bristol blower by the name of Henry Ricketts developed a revolutionary, hand-operated, split mould, made of two hollow blocks of iron. This made it possible, for the first time, for makers to blow the whole bottle, and not just the body of a bottle, in a mould. It also allowed lettering to be embossed onto the glass, enabling brewers to mark their wares with their signature. But, still, beer in bottles was a rare sight. It took another twenty-four years and an act of Parliament to really provide beer makers with the incentive to package beer on a grand scale. In 1845 Excise Acts which had imposed a tax of 8/9d per hundredweight on glass bottles were repealed. The price of glassware was consequently reduced and this led to the wider use of glasses in pubs to replace pewter tankards (and so helped the clear pale ales of Burton to outshine the murky porters of London). It also gave an impetus to the take-home trade. Brewers seized the opportunity: Whitbread, Worthington and Bass were among the most adventurous and soon became the leading purveyors of bottled beers. Their business was boosted by the expansion in the railway network, which enabled crates of ale, or casks for bottling off-site, to be quickly and easily transported. Further advances in bottling technology, which improved the product and streamlined production, aided their growth. In 1872 an internal screw stopper was invented as a replacement for the cork by the Englishman Henry Barrett. His device was superseded to a large degree twenty years later when William Painter of Baltimore introduced the crown cork. In the meantime, around 1880, semi-automatic bottle-making machinery came into operation. By 1904 the first fully automatic bottle-making equipment was put into use at the Toledo Glass Company in the USA. Bottling beer had become cheap, quick and efficient.

For the beer enthusiast, however, progress is not always a good thing. As the technology for producing glassware was developing, so was the technology for producing the beer to fill it. In 1866 the great Louis Pasteur published his *Etudes sur le vin*, a scientific study of wine which led him to extol the merits of heat-treatment in order to control fermentation and so to prevent the wine going off. By around 1870 he had turned his attention to beer and was experimenting in Copenhagen before publishing his *Etudes sur la bière* in 1871. He found that, by heating beer to around 57° C (135° F) for a few minutes, he could prevent abnormal fermentation taking place. However, he may have been beaten to the punch as far as beer is concerned, as brewers and scientists in Germany and Austria, no doubt inspired by Pasteur's work with wine, had already begun to tamper with beer production.

By the 1920s the benefits of pasteurisation in cutting back bacterial infection had come to be widely recognised by bottling brewers. In 1923, for instance, Whitbread took over the smaller, but more technologically advanced, Forest Hill Brewery, largely to acquire its skill in bottling processed beers. At Forest Hill they matured and filtered the beers before bottling and had gained expertise in carbonating beer. As Whitbread took the techniques on board, 'Bright to the last drop' became a familiar slogan for the company's bottled beers. By December 1930 all but one of Whitbread's bottled beers (its celebrated Stout) were bright. Four or five decades before the cask ale crisis which saw the birth of CAMRA, real beer already had its back to the wall.

There appeared to be little reaction to the new-fangled bottled beers other than favourable, if you listen to the brewers. Consequently, by the time CAMRA did find its feet, there were only five regularly produced bottle-conditioned beers to be found. These 'classics', as long-standing members will recite to you, were Worthington White Shield, Thomas Hardy's Ale, Gale's Prize Old Ale, Courage Imperial Russian Stout and Guinness Extra Stout. Of these, Guinness is no longer with us, having been sacrificed to the pasteuriser in 1993, but more about the others can be found in the feature headed *The Classics*.

The Renaissance

So where has the revival come from? Well, we can start looking in the unlikely back-drop of Mexico. While 'serious' drinkers were busily deriding the practice of stuffing lime into the necks of Corona lager bottles, they were mostly ignoring the fact that glassware had come back into fashion, at the expense of the uglier canned beer market. As for reviving real ale in a bottle, CAMRA played its part by introducing a new category for the product in the *Champion Beer of Britain* awards of 1991. The renais-sance in cask real ale has also had a knock-on effect, as has the innovative approach of the microbrewers, and the importing of cloudy German wheat beers and Belgian ales may have had a say, too. And, crucially, bigger brewers with an eye on their reputa-tions, can now bottle-condition their beers with greater confidence thanks to modern, efficient and sterile bottling equipment, stronger glassware and techniques like the acid washing of priming yeast to reduce the risk of infection.

What's more, it looks as if the revival is set to continue. As this book went to press, the Government was considering amending the Guest Beer Law so that it embraced bottle-conditioned beers. The law, as it was introduced in 1990, allowed tenants of national brewers' pubs to stock a cask-conditioned real ale of their own choosing, irrespective of any beer tie which was in place on their pub. The fairness of this law was contested in 1996 by the European Commission which argued that it dis-criminated against continental breweries that, by and large, did not produce cask beer. CAMRA and other worried parties pointed out that there were dozens if not hun-dreds of European beers which would have qualified for guest beer status and the mat-ter now appears to have been resolved with a compromise. What is proposed is that, in addition to a guest *cask-conditioned* beer, the publicans concerned can now also stock a guest *bottle-conditioned* beer of their own choosing. If the Government, as is expected, ratifies this change, it will provide a massive boost for brewers of bottle-conditioned beers and the publication of this guide will be particularly opportune.

This legal change may help bottle-conditioning become more than the gimmicky fad some have suggested it to be. It's true that yeast in the bottle (albeit it thoroughly traditional) is a novelty for today's drinker and provides a neat hook for the sales and marketing men. But if it is a fad, at least it's one which expands choice and quality for the consumer who benefits from the improvement in taste which bottle-conditioning brings: freshness, full flavours and natural condition over dead beer, the stale tang of pasteurisation and the sickly fizz of added CO_2

Other observers see bottle-conditioning as an easy way for brewers to use up excess cask beer, and there are some who contest the value of the yeast in certain bottles, claiming it to be little more than cosmetic. But, even if we accept that, on occasion, they may be right, it still means that real ale in a bottle is back and, for the sake of the many fine beers which lead this revolution we should do everything we can to hold on to it.

How To Keep And Serve Bottle-Conditioned Beers

All today's bottled beers are stamped with a 'best before' date. This is a legal requirement and is designed to ensure that customers are not saddled with old and tired stock. For filtered and pasteurised beers the best before date is important. Such beers cannot be consumed with any confidence beyond this time. For bottle-conditioned beers, however, with their life-giving yeast, the best before date is often nominal, put in place to pacify the Trading Standards people but bearing no reflection of the quality of the beer before or after this time. Indeed, some brewers wryly suggest that their mark should be a 'best after' date, so well do their beers continue to mature beyond the prescribed limit.

As evidence of this phenomenon, it is interesting to cite the 1990 *Good Beer Guide,* in which Roger Protz described how Worthington White Shield, according to devotees, mellowed over time, having a 'sickness period' between six and nine months after bottling, when it tasted below par, but then coming back into a drinkable state again. One could also recall stories of cases of Thomas Hardy's Ale and Gale's Prize Old Ale being purchased for infants at christening time and consumed on the child's twenty-first birthday to gasps of delight. But he who plays the waiting game chances his arm. There is no guarantee that such beers will continue to improve over a long period. They will change, certainly, as they mature, but whether that change will be for the better no one can honestly say. That should not deter anyone from experimenting with bottle-conditioned beers, providing, of course, a few ground rules are followed.

The first is that bottled beers, generally, should be kept in the dark. You will notice that nearly all the bottles are dark in colour (mostly brown).

This is for a purpose. The opacity of the glass protects the beer from being 'sunstruck'. This is a chemical reaction caused by the action of sunlight or other bright lights on the beer and leads to unpleasant flavours and unsavoury aromas. To help the bottles do their job, drinkers should ensure that any beers stored for a length of time are tucked away in a light-free zone.

The second rule to follow is that bottle-conditioned beers should be kept cool. As with all living food stuffs, the low temperature preserves the beer. If the beer is corked (as Gale's Prize Old Ale), there is also a small chance that the cork will pop out in warm conditions. Some brewers advocate keeping bottles at a higher temperature to begin with, to get the yeast working and the secondary fermentation underway, then cooling the beer until you wish to drink it. Other brewers propose that you generally keep their beer cool but allow it some time in a warmer environment just before you finally chill it ready for serving. This helps the beer generate a bit more natural fizz on opening. Each beer has its own recommended serving temperature and this is outlined within each entry in this book.

Further guidance relates to the position of bottles. Most are recommended for storage upright, but corked bottles are best suited to laying down, to keep the cork moist. If you do lay some down, remember to put them back upright a couple of days before drinking to allow the sediment to settle at the bottom of the bottle.

This 'problem' of sediment is not as great as the proponents of filtering would make out. It is true that some beers carry a heavy yeast content which can fall like fine sand into your glass, making the beer cloudy and possibly resulting in an unpleasant last mouthful. It is my experience, though, that most of the yeasts used today are remarkably sticky and seem almost painted onto the bottom of the bottle. Whereas in the past drinkers with shaky hands fretted over one long, slow, careful pour to extract as much beer and a minimum of yeast from the bottle, I have found beers which allow up to three separate pours and even then barely colour the glass with yeast. All the same, caution should be the watchword if you don't care for a yeasty drink, but it's worth reminding readers that the yeast, in most cases, will cause you no harm. The slight exception is for gout sufferers who may find their condition exacerbated by the protein in the yeast. Indeed, many drinkers eagerly await the last yeasty dregs and some beers are designed to be drunk cloudy and carry instructions accordingly.

From Bottle To Glass

When it comes to pouring and tasting bottled beers, once again there are accepted techniques for gaining maximum enjoyment. The first and paramount rule is: don't choose a warm glass. This major failing of too many barmen shouldn't be replicated in your own home. The warmth of the glass not only negates any cooling you may have arranged for the bottles but also speeds up flavour loss and oxidation. Secondly, if you can, choose a glass which enhances the appreciation of the style of beer you're drinking. A trip to Belgium will quickly reveal how Belgian brewers produce special branded glasses for each of their beers. This is not entirely a marketing exercise but is designed to ensure that the maximum enjoyment is gleaned from each brew. The shape of the glass helps bring out the best qualities of the beer. For instance, they provide wide-rim glasses for aromatic beers, narrow-topped glasses for beers which are meant to hold their fizz, such as Champagne-like fruit beers, and rounded-bottomed glasses which warm nicely in the hand for rich, strong ales which change character as their temperature rises. Consider the beer you're sampling and see if you have a glass to match. Whichever glass you select, rinse it first with cold water. This helps reduce the risk of fobbing if the beer is lively.

One point I would make at this stage is that by drinking bottle-conditioned beers at home you have the advantage over cask beer drinkers in the pub because you can dictate not only your own glassware but also the amount of beer you put into it. Swirling a small quantity in a glass with a slightly turned-in top, designed to hold in aromas, is a much easier way of assessing the nose of a beer than trying to stick your beak into a brim-full pint − a fact, I feel, which explains why some pub drinkers scoff at enthusiasts who discuss such qualities as the beer's 'bouquet'.

The Tasting Experience

Which leads us on nicely to the tasting experience. The first point I would make is that tasting anything is a subjective matter. Everyone's taste perceptions differ. Your taste detection (of bitterness, hoppiness, sweetness, maltiness, etc.) may not be as great as your neighbour's but your tasting experience may be greater, allowing you to recall and compare exotic flavours like kiwi fruit, mangoes or black cherries, that he has never encountered. What I have attempted to do in this book is merely pick out the flavours that were obvious to me. I have sought the brewers' own views on the taste of their beers and have taken these into consideration to provide a more balanced description. But the tasting notes I have put forward are merely a snapshot. As the very merit of bottle-conditioned beers lies in the fact that they mature in the bottle, the notes should only be used as a guide to the broad flavourings and the general style of the beer. I would urge you to taste for yourself and see what you can find.

The first stage of tasting comes not with the mouth, or the nose, but with the eye. There is no doubt that you can be positively or negatively led towards a beer simply from liking or disliking its appearance. The colour may be appealing or unattractive, but a greater factor is the condition. A flat, lifeless beer appears as appetising as a soggy tomato sandwich, even though there may be more carbonation apparent later on the tongue. Go for the aroma next. As suggested above, pour a little into the glass (if you can trust the sediment to allow you a second pour), give it a good swirl then take a deep sniff. I find I need a few sniffs to really sort out the complex scents which arise. These come from the various ingredients used in the brew (malt, hops, etc.), but also result from the brewing process which throws up the most unlikely characteristics, like exotic fruits. These aromatic emissions are known as esters and arise from the activity of the yeast. In lower gravity beers, the fruitiness is usually light and citric; in stronger, heavy beers more pronounced fruity scents like banana and pear drops may be apparent. When you move onto drinking the beer, the aroma element is still active, particularly when you swallow and the aroma escapes from the back of your throat through your nose.

When tasting beer, give it some time in your mouth for full appreciation. You may be tempted to knock it back, but it pays dividends to wash the beer over your tongue, allowing each flavour-sensitive part to do its job and pick up the salt, sour, sweet and bitter characteristics and other flavours you may recognise. You will also be able to judge the body (is it light or heavy, smooth or rough, creamy or grainy?) and the degree of condition (the amount of dissolved carbon dioxide in the beer). Without good condition, a beer is very unappealing and too flat on the tongue; too much condition and the beer can be sharp and prickly to drink.

Most beer descriptions centre on malt and hops, these being the main components of the beer. For the uninitiated, malt is usually sweetish (from the maltose sugar it contains) and can have a grainy, nutty or biscuity taste. Dark malts bring roasted flavours, including coffee and chocolate. Malt can also be responsible for dryness in a beer. Hops provide bitterness but much more besides. They can taste peppery, herbal, resinous, citric, floral and grassy. On top of malt and hops, fruity esters introduce all sorts of intriguing flavours.

Thankfully, beer tasting, unlike wine tasting, requires you to swallow and not spit, as the aftertaste is all important. How often have you sat in a pub and enjoyed the long, lingering taste in your mouth and throat after a good gulp of beer? You probably recognise, too, that this aftertaste is not quite the same as the beer tastes in the mouth. This is because, depending on the brew, certain attributes (particularly bitterness) last longer or become more apparent later.

One major factor about beer tasting which I think is too often overlooked is quantity. Because beer is usually so much weaker than wine, it can be drunk in greater volume, and there's no question that your opinion of a beer can change the more you drink (even before you reach the intoxication stage). So why confine beer tastings to the odd sip? Drink up the bottle and then make up your mind. See how your perceptions have altered since the first mouthful.

If, like me, you manage to sample most of the beers in this book, you will have learned a lot about tasting beer and, I'm sure, never again will you consider discussing beer in simple black and white terms such as 'a hoppy bitter' or 'a malty mild'. You will also have realised that the bottled beer world is becoming more colourful by the day.

By the time the next edition is published who knows how many bottle-conditioned beers we will have to enjoy. Happy drinking!

Jeff Evans, Newbury, 1997

Acknowledgements

The author would like to thank numerous people who have been of great assistance in the compilation of this book. These include all the brewers who kindly forwarded details of their beers and sample bottles; the leading supermarket chains who provided information about the beers they stock; Peter Ward and Roger Wharton at Thomas Hardy Brewery; Derek Lowe at Gale's Brewery; Bill King at King & Barnes Brewery; Cheryl Finch at Bass; Kirstin Fitzgerald at Scottish Courage; Steve Wellington and Diana Lay at the Bass Museum; Nicholas Redman at the Whitbread Archive; Dr Keith Thomas at Brewlab, University of Sunderland; Gray Olliver of Wessex Brewers; Iain Loe, CAMRA's Research Manager; and CAMRA's many brewery liaison officers.

The Classics

The term 'classic' has several meanings. In one respect, it can refer to something of the highest order, and in this context may be applied to many of the beers featured in this book. It can also mean something which is used as a model or a guide, something which provides the inspiration for followers. It is in this latter respect that the four beers highlighted in this feature are justly described as 'classics'.

Of course, classic also refers to antiquity and again our four beers fit the bill. The four are the last surviving bottle-conditioned beers of pre-CAMRA days, beers which have withstood the ravages of pasteurisation and artificial carbonation for decades, if not centuries, and which in recent years have carried the torch for the new generation of bottled real ales. This chapter is written to honour the mighty Thomas Hardy's Ale, Prize Old Ale, Imperial Russian Stout and Worthington White Shield, but also to mourn the loss of another classic, Guinness Original (née Extra Stout).

If ever an example is needed of the insensitivity of a multi-national company to consumers' wishes, the attitude of Guinness to its bottled beer devotees will stand out. Unpasteurised Guinness Original was a cult beer, attracting aficionados of both sexes and of all ages. Many a real ale drinker gasped a sigh of relief on seeing the pert little bottles tucked away behind the bar in an otherwise cheerless, keg-only pub. This was a beer of character and complexity, a beer for connoisseurs, a beer with a heritage. But for Guinness it was a nuisance. Despite selling quantities which would make a size-able British regional, let alone a microbrewer, ecstatic (it amounted to nearly a quarter of all Guinness's bottled trade), it was deemed to be uneconomic. In a letter to CAMRA's *What's Brewing* newspaper in January 1993, Marketing Director Robert MacNevin also cited the lack of consistency of the beer as a reason for its demise and suggested that 'pre-conditioning' at the brewery (i.e. giving it the keg treatment) would stabilise the beer and help to 'preserve its taste'. The fact that this particular kite had been flown by Watneys and their contemporaries twenty years earlier and been comprehensively shot down by consumers who formed CAMRA appeared to have been lost on Mr MacNevin. But, getting back to the core of his argument, so what if the beer does change slightly from brew to brew and as it ages? That, surely, is the beauty of living beers. Together with the wonderful fresh flavours they offer, it is the reason why real ales on draught have flourished and why so many brewers have now turned once again to real bottled beers. Many of these bottles are sold in pubs as well as off-licences, so the other argument that Mr MacNevin pursued in his letter, that the bottled beer market in the on-trade (real Guinness's stamping ground – off-sales had been pasteurised for some time) was in decline also now looks shaky. Given the likely extension to the Guest Beer Law to allow pubs to stock a guest bottle-conditioned beer, as well as a guest draught real ale, perhaps Guinness could be encouraged to have a change of heart. The ironic downside of this would be that, if it had the will, Guinness could quickly swallow up much of this new guest beer market.

Worthington White Shield

Like Guinness, White Shield was always the great standby in a keg pub. Sadly, in my experience, not enough keg pubs (even Bass keg pubs) have been bothered to stock it. One pub near my home in Berkshire thankfully always did, up to a change of regime a few years ago. I say thankfully because the draught ale was always dire through lack of turnover but the White Shield magnificent because it had been gathering dust on the shelf for a couple of years through the same lack of custom.

White Shield was first brewed in the early 19th century, probably around the 1820s. It was a bottled version of the Burton India Pale Ales, strong beers with high hop contents. Though Worthington brewed it, they did not bottle it, instead shipping the beer in casks out to smaller brewers or bottlers around the country who placed their names on the label. The instruction booklets issued to these concerns make fascinating reading. They provide guidance on stillage and pegging the casks, and advise that the beer would be ready for bottling about ten–fourteen days after stillaging in winter, seven–ten days in summer. Conditioning in the bottle was to take place on site for five weeks in winter and four at warmer times, but on no account should conditioning be accelerated by artificially warming the bottles.

The same advice was given to bottlers of Bass Red Triangle when Bass and Worthington joined forces. Red Triangle was the Bass equivalent of White Shield and was first sold in the 1850s. It lost ground when the pasteurised and carbonated Blue Triangle was introduced in 1934 and by the 1960s it was in serious decline, to the point where the original Red Triangle recipe was discarded and it became the same brew as White Shield, albeit under a different label. By 1970 Red Triangle had disappeared altogether.

Returning to White Shield itself, the beer was not formally known as White Shield until recent times. The label has carried various titles, including Worthington's India Pale Ale, Worthington's Fine Burton Ale and Worthington's Original Pale Ale. Today the marketing men have caught up: the label reads Worthington's White Shield Fine Strong Ale. Indeed, the White Shield label is a labologist's dream, so much has it changed over the years whilst appearing not to have changed at all. The shield itself, complete with dagger, has been ever-present (it is in fact one of the world's oldest registered trademarks), but the wording below it has been altered as the brew has moved from its original home to Sheffield and on to its present site, the Cape Hill brewery in Birmingham, the words Burton-upon-Trent being subtly forgotten in the re-design.

In the old days, the label used to be notched on the right hand side to indicate

Most people would never drink a whole bottle of White Shield

During its lifetime many traditions and methods have grown up around the pouring of White Shield. In fact, there is quite an art to pouring a White Shield.

And if you've never poured it before you might find it a bit tricky. But keep at it. Because, of course, after the first taste you're bound to want to keep practising.

1. The point to remember when pouring White Shield is to leave the last tablespoon of beer with the sediment in the bottom of the bottle.

2. Pour at eye level (you have to watch for that sediment), keeping the bottle and the glass almost horizontal. Then, without resting the bottle on the rim of the glass pour the beer along the glass very slowly.

3. Now gradually straighten the glass as it fills – but avoid any violent movement of the bottle which would disturb the sediment.

4. You should now have a beautifully clear glass of White Shield and a bottle with the sediment in. If you didn't pour it to your own satisfaction maybe a little homework is called for. But remember, it's your White Shield – never let anyone else pour it for you!

On the other hand...

There are two other schools of thought to the pouring of White Shield.

One is practised by the White Shield brewers. That is to pour the White Shield in the approved manner leaving the sediment in the bottle, drink the beer and then knock back the sediment at the end.

The other is also to pour White Shield in the approved manner, but then tip the natural sediment in and watch the goodness start to sink to the bottom.

in which quarter of the year the beer had been bottled, with a number printed in the centre revealing in which week of the quarter. Four notches and the printed number one meant that the beer had been produced in the first week of the fourth quarter (i.e. the first week of October). Notches made on the left hand side were technical codes for the brewers. All this has now been supplanted by the less arcane best before date in the top left corner of the label.

The glassware has also changed with the times. In 1992 the beer was re-launched in a fancy non-returnable bottle with wider shoulders and a bulbous neck, though this now seems to have given way to a more traditional White Shield bottle. The beer even has its own peculiar glass. It is stemmed and designed to hold the exact quantity from a careful pouring.

Officially known as a 'Worthington', it is the vessel to use, according to purists, for there is a declared skill to pouring a bottle of White Shield. Written instructions exist (see illustration on page 15) and certificates have been awarded to accomplished pourers during brewery visits.

The purpose of the elaborate pouring procedure is to ensure that all the yeast sediment remains in the bottle. However, there is less danger today of yeast clouding your glass because with the aforementioned re-launch came a switch of yeast strains. The new yeast (added to the bottle to replace yeast filtered out after primary fermentation) is stickier than the old, as well as being less copious. But this is not the only change the beer has undergone, much to the chagrin of committed drinkers who complain that the beer is not what it used to be. Its strong herbal aroma has been reined back to broaden its appeal to a wider cross-section of drinkers and the beer has been made more 'subtle', according to Bass. Even the hops have been changed. The brew now incorporates Eroica and Northern Brewer varieties, whereas previously Challenger and Northdown were the chosen strains. Another major change has been in the fermentation procedure. In former days, like Draught Bass, White Shield was brewed using the Burton Union system in which beer was fermented in wooden casks and allowed to spill over into open troughs before running back into the cask, leaving yeast behind. At the time, the beer was advertised with the slogan 'Brewed in the wood, matures in the bottle'. The Unions were removed in the early 1980s and only Marston's now has such a system. When all this is taken into account, the hardened enthusiast will tell you that White Shield is not as good as before. I haven't been drinking it for decades so I can't confirm this. But I can declare that it's still an exceptionally fine beer.

Courage Imperial Russian Stout

Even before strong pale ales were being shipped around the world to India, Britain already had a popular export beer. The trade was with cold countries not hot ones, so the beer was substantially different: a dark, heavy, nourishing brew rather than a crisp, hoppy quencher. Scottish Courage's Imperial Russian Stout is the best-known relic of this long-gone age and virtually extinct beer style. Strong and warming enough to keep out a Siberian winter, it's origins date back to the 1780s at a time when trade with Baltic countries was on a high. Finland, Germany, Poland and Prussia were among the nations which enjoyed British exports but it was in Russia that this beer gained its most appreciative audience. The beer was rolled aboard ship in hogsheads and rolled off at the other end to be bottled and marketed by a firm known as Le Coq. Their message was that the beer was a great medicinal tonic and their sales success was significantly enhanced by the fact that it became a firm favourite of Empress Catherine the Great. (Further imperial patronage came over a hundred years later when the beer was awarded a warrant by Empress Alexandra to supply the royal court, in recognition of Le Coq's generosity in donating 5,000 bottles to hospitals in which the Empress took a personal interest.) Le Coq was a British company, established by a Belgian. It survived trading problems brought on by the Napoleonic Wars and capitalised on the success of Russian Stout by setting up its own brewery in Tartu, Estonia. This was nationalised after the Russian Revolution in 1917 and led to a lengthy wrangle over compensation which was only resolved in 1971.

At the outset, Imperial Russian Stout was brewed by a London company, Barclay, Perkins & Co. Founded in 1781, it was based at the Thames-side Anchor Brewery and finally disappeared after merging with Courage in 1955. Despite the rationalisation which plagued British brewing in the 1960s and 1970s, Courage, to its credit, kept Imperial Russian Stout alive, albeit with ever more sporadic brews. The last took place at John Smith's Brewery in Tadcaster in 1993 and, with stocks still in hand, no date has yet been set for another batch. Trade within the UK has largely been centred in pubs around London and the South-East, where loyal supporters have called on their barmen to crack open one of the nip bottles for a nightcap at the end of an evening. Others have been known to add the bottle to a glass of bitter for an unusual version of a black and tan. The beer is probably more in demand outside the UK these days, in countries with a longer history of enjoying connoisseur bottled beers, countries like Belgium and Holland, but also the less likely destinations of Tenerife, Bermuda and Italy.

Imperial Russian Stout is a single varietal beer, using just Target hops, and plenty of them (around 24 lbs per barrel). This high hop rate is a relic of the export shipping days, when (just as for IPAs), heavy hopping ensured the beer remained free from infection on the long sea journeys. The hops also provide sound bitterness to balance the winey, burnt maltiness which comes from a combination of pale, amber and black malts and brewing sugar. The original gravity is 1098, giving, after fermentation, an ABV of ten per cent. This strength and body, like its hoppiness, were vital to its export success. Such a high gravity ensured that the beer enjoyed a good secondary conditioning aboard ship and was fresh on arrival.

At John Smith's each brew is given a week's conditioning at 20° C, and up to two months' cold conditioning at before bottling takes place, although this is a less romantic substitute for the year's maturation in oak casks which the beer enjoyed when brewed in London. The bottling procedure is elementary. The beer is not filtered, re-seeded with yeast or primed with sugars: it is bottled 'as it comes'.

How long this beer lasts in the bottle is anyone's guess. There are rumours of finding 25-year-old samples at the bottom of the sea which have been in wonderful condition, but the best I can honestly tell you is that the 1993 batch is still eminently drinkable and shows no sign of deteriorating.

Gale's Prize Old Ale

Gale's Prize Old Ale has long been famous as the beer in a corked bottle. But there's more to this complex, unique brew than a lump of wood in its neck. At a heady nine per cent alcohol, it is rich and full, with more in common with a red wine than a hoppy session bitter. It is a true classic and, despite providing only a fraction of the Gale's business, it has become central to the brewery's image as a traditional brewer of quality beers.

The recipe – involving pale ale and black malts, with Fuggle and Golding hops – was brought to Hampshire by a Yorkshire brewer named Steel in the 1920s. Where he picked up the recipe is unknown. Today's head brewer, Derek Lowe, has been in charge of the beer since his arrival at Gale's in 1981. He's made one or two changes but is committed to the tradition of POA. The beer is still boiled in the same old copper for two long hours and is usually fermented in one of two original 1920s vessels. One move he has made is to swap the old wooden hogsheads in which the beer was matured for modern conditioning tanks. The brewery no longer had a cooper and the taste variations from the various hogsheads meant that each year's brew needed to be blended to ensure consistency. Derek also sees another benefit in the switch to metal. He claims it gives the beer a cleaner taste. But those who lament the loss of wood can derive some comfort from the fact that tradition has had the last laugh: two of the new tanks are containers which used to hold tankered-in lager for kegging, a practice Gale's have now abandoned.

POA is conditioned at the brewery for at least six months (when it is fined), and possibly up to twelve, but time itself is less important now than in the early days. Of greater significance is the condition of the beer, its alcohol content and its character, so the beer may be bottled earlier than in the past but with greater assurance of its consistency. Before bottling, the beer is not primed with sugar, but more yeast – the same as used in all Gale's brews – is added if required. (In the 1960s, POA was brewed using yeast from Marston's Brewery, collected by the churn from Marston's depot in neighbouring Winchester.) Until mid-1997 bottling was still done by hand, from rinsing the new glassware to sticking on the labels and ensuring the cork was squeezed into place. The installation of a new, small bottling line has now streamlined this activity.

The famous cork has its quaintness but also its drawbacks. It needs to be kept moist, so Gale's advise laying the beer on its side during storage, before bringing it back upright for 48 hours prior to drinking. The cork may also present a problem if the beer is kept too warm and the beer ferments too vigorously in the bottle. This once happened on a hot New York quayside. The beer arrived on the 4th July, with the local dockers on holiday. The bottles stood unprotected and some of the corks blew. It's not a problem which should be exaggerated, however, as only forty-nine bottles out of over a hundred cases were affected even then.

If there is a flaw in the brewery's handling of this ale it is in the archiving of it. Sadly, there has been no systematic storage of the beer's vintages, which means that a scientific vertical tasting is not possible, but there are now plans to label each bottle with the year of production. This will be the latest change in a series of modifications to the glassware. The label has been re-designed on a number of occasions and it now includes an individual number to allow the brewery to monitor quality. The old foil wrapping around the cork has also been lost and has been replaced by a more functional plastic hood, and the bottle itself has changed. It is a distinctive half-pint (275 ml) bottle which Gale's designed and hold the copyright for. The broad-shouldered shape remains the same as ever but the need for more information to be posted on the back for exporting purposes has led to the embossed Gale's logo disappearing and being replaced by the name of the company curved around the base of the neck.

These modifications reflect the brewery's intention to keep Prize Old Ale at the forefront of their activity, even though its volumes remain modest. Derek assures me that Gale's have never considered dropping the beer and, indeed, all the talk these days is about improving sales and building up the export market. This is a far cry from the days when the beer was actually rationed. Up until the early 1980s, so little was produced that Gale's pubs were only allowed one case a fortnight, and eagerly awaited it appeared to be. But when the restriction was lifted the expected increase in orders failed to materialise. It seems that Gale's drinkers appreciated this maverick beer like the rest of us, as a little treat every now and then and not as an everyday refresher.

Derek Lowe confirms that POA will improve with age, for at least up to five years. He hesitates about recommending longer storage, even though some excellent 20-year-old bottles have been tried. But the beer can also be drunk young: after bottling it is kept for three months at the brewery so it is not what you might call 'green'. The samples I tried carried a best before date of September 2001 and so could definitely be considered to be on the young side. This may have been the cause of the rather low condition which rendered the beer slightly flat on the tongue, although the nose and taste were certainly not disappointing. Deep, winey fruitiness and creamy vanilla in the aroma were followed by a powerful, mouth-tingling flavour of various fruits mixed with peppery hop bitterness. Dry, bitter fruit edged out sweetness in the finish. Each bottle of Prize Old Ale should become drier and more complex as the years roll by.

Most of today's production is exported to Japan and the USA. In the UK, only Gale's pubs, specialist beer shops, the odd local supermarket and a few wholesalers take supplies. Each brew is thirty barrels in length and produces 720 cases of twenty-four bottles, although some is kept back to be blended with the brewery's Butser Bitter to create the dark cask beer Winter Brew (formerly known as 5X). POA used to be brewed only once a month, but now goes in once a fortnight or even more frequently, and, with the new bottling line on stream, the incentive may be there to step up production even further. Or Gale's might turn their attention to other bottle-conditioned beers to build on their recent commemorative offerings like Victory Ale, D-Day Ale and CAMRA's 25th Birthday Ale.

Thomas Hardy's Ale

Thomas Hardy's Ale was once sold to the world as 'The Rarest Ale in Britain'. Anyone who has tried to find this beer in the UK outside its native Dorset would happily concur with this boast as it's not the sort of beer that's easy to pick up in a supermarket. But, as is often the case, the harder the search, the more enjoyable the discovery.

This complex, bottle-conditioned beer at 12 per cent ABV was created by Eldridge Pope in 1968 as a memorial to the Wessex writer who had died forty years earlier, but it's the sort of strong, distinctive brew you imagine has been around for centuries. Its inspiration was a passage in Hardy's novel *The Trumpet-Major* which described Dorchester's strong beer as 'full in body, yet brisk as a volcano', its hue as 'luminous as an autumn sunset'. Clearly, Hardy was a man who liked his ale.

Today's head brewer, Roger Wharton, doubts whether the ale replicates any particular beer from Hardy's day. It is brewed from a half-and-half combination of pale ale and – surprisingly – pale lager malts, with no adjuncts. Around 50 barrels are produced at a time, from a mash with a mighty original gravity of 1125. In fact the mash yields some 200 barrels of wort but 150 are watered down and turned into EP Extra Smooth – a classic bottle-conditioned beer parti-gyled with a nitrokeg bitter: truly the sublime and the ridiculous.

Hardy's Ale is brewed, fittingly, in the company's old brewhouse, using the smaller of two coppers, where a hefty five pounds of whole Golding hops per barrel balance the heavily malty wort. Fermentation takes place in a 75-barrel vessel, allowing room for a giant foam head which the yeast throws up. The head climbs up to eight feet above the wort and plastic extensions have to be added to keep it in the vessel.

Though the beer is called 'Ale', its yeast is actually a Bavarian bottle-conditioning yeast which sinks to the bottom, allowing the beer to be easily drawn off after two-three weeks. Six–seven months of warm-conditioning follows in a tank where another charge of hops and more yeast are added. Here the beer is blended, if necessary, with beer from the same vintage, to ensure consistency of colour, taste and strength. Before bottling, a few months of cold tank treatment (-2° C) precipitates the protein and settles   the yeast. The ale is drawn off the sediment into a bright beer tank, where yet more yeast (acid-washed to cut down on infection) is added. Unprimed, the beer is bottled the same day.

The bottle size has changed on a number of occasions. Bottle number one, carefully cossetted at the brewery, is an 18 oz bottle, corked and waxed. Later, 180 ml (nip) bottles went on sale in the UK while the export version went out in 330s. Today all bottles are 330 ml, each individually numbered and carrying the famous *Trumpet-Major* quote which inspired the beer. There have also been special editions. In 1990, for instance, on the 150th anniversary of Thomas Hardy's birth, a limited supply of just 2,700 special 330 ml bottles was produced.

The label boasts that the beer will 'last at least 25 years' and, traditionally, the brewery has recommended that drinkers don't touch a drop until it is three, or even, five years old. Roger Wharton is less rigid and, whilst he appreciates older bottles, he also suggests trying the beer younger. His advice is to store it at home at room temperature, perhaps even a little warmer for the first few months, just to ensure the yeast gets to work and builds up the condition. 'Drink it from a brandy balloon and notice how the flavours and aromas develop between sips' is his tasting guidance.

I tried a bottle from the 1988 vintage and admired its dark ruby red colour. The aroma was magnificent, fruity and sherry-like, with a hint of wood behind. On the tongue, the condition was low but not unappealing and the mouthfilling taste was of rich sweetness well balanced by hop bitterness. Strawberries lurked in the background and a syrupy finish warmed the throat.

Today about 250,000 bottles of Thomas Hardy's Ale are produced each year, with the main markets being export, largely the USA, Italy, France and Scandinavia. In the UK, the best place to look is still in Eldridge Pope pubs – which goes some way to confirming its title of 'The Rarest Ale in Britain'.

How The Guide Is Organised

The CAMRA Guide to Real Ale in a Bottle contains details of all bottle-conditioned beers being brewed in the UK at the time of going to press. Others brewers have been known to produce bottle-conditioned beers from time to time, or were planning to do so when contacted, so keep an eye open for their products. These include Young's, Church End, Worth, Little Avenham and Lugton breweries.

The beers are listed by brewery (which is briefly described), with independent breweries first and national breweries at the end. Within each brewery, beers are listed by increasing order of strength. For each beer the following information is given: alcohol by volume percentage (ABV), bottle size, suggested serving temperature, ingredients and availability.

The tasting notes featured are the views of the author, unless otherwise stated. As bottle-conditioned beers are likely to change character during their shelf-life, the flavour balance and level of condition may well vary. These notes are therefore offered only as a basic guide to the type of beer in the bottle.

For more details of all the breweries featured in this book, and for information about the cask-conditioned beers they produce, see CAMRA's Good Beer Guide (published annually).

Where to Buy Bottle-Conditioned Beers

Where beers are actually sold is inevitably subject to change so it is suggested that readers contact the brewery for up to date details of shops which sell their beers. Good places to track down bottle-conditioned beers are specialist off-licences. There are now scores of these across the UK, emulating the success of outlets like The Beer Shop in Pitfield Street, London, telephone (0171) 739 3701. There are also mail order companies which specialise in beer. These include The Beer Cellar, 31 Norwich Road, Strumpshaw, Norwich, Norfolk NR13 4AG, telephone (01603) 714884. You can also try farm shops and craft centres near the breweries themselves.

On the high street, you can of course look in at Tesco, Sainsbury, Waitrose, Asda and the other leading supermarkets, whose range of bottle-conditioned beers has admirably expanded in recent years. Some, particularly Tesco, stock local beers. Amongst the chain off-licences, the best bottle-conditioned beer choice is at Oddbins, but smaller companies like Unwins also sell a few examples and offer occasional bottle-conditioned guests.

The Independents

Ash Vine

Ash Vine Brewery (South West) Ltd., The White Hart, Trudoxhill, Frome, Somerset BA11 5DP. Tel./Fax (01373) 836344

Ash Vine Brewery was set up in 1987 near Taunton, but moved to the White Hart pub in 1989.

Penguin Porter

ABV 4.2%	Bottle size 500 ml	Serve at 13°C

Ingredients	Maris Otter black, pale and crystal malts; Challenger and Golding hops

A 'Porter that protects penguins', according to the label. This beer was first produced in 1995 and a small donation for every bottle sold goes to help raise funds for Penguin World at Marwell Zoo. Modestly describing itself on earlier labels as a 'black and white sensation', Penguin Porter is claimed to age very well, improving for at least six months to develop 'an exquisite chocolate flavour'. It's not a special brew for the bottle: it's actually the brewery's Black Bess Porter simply bottled from a conditioning tank, with no filtration, primings or new yeast. The best before date is set nine months from bottling time. Drink it with or without the yeast sediment..

Tasting Notes

A smooth, fruity and chocolatey, dark red/brown brew with some liquorice in the taste. Dry bitterness and roast grain come through in the lingering finish. Easy drinking and not too heavy. A little flat on the tongue; loose, light sediment.

Availability

From local Sainsbury, Tesco, Waitrose, Co-op, Firkin off-licences, smaller off-licences and The Beer Cellar (mail order).

Hop & Glory

ABV 5%	Bottle size 500 ml	Serve at 13° C

Ingredients Maris Otter pale malt; Challenger and Golding hops

Like Penguin Porter, this strong pale ale is a bottle-conditioned version of a cask beer, this time without a name change. It first found its way into bottle in 1995 and is exactly the same brew as Hop & Glory cask. It's very much the brewery's major bottled product and has led the way for some microbrewers into the supermarkets. This is thanks, to some degree, to its idyllic label, which emphasises the related traditions of village green cricket and quality English ale, depicting the legendary WG Grace in the throes of executing the perfect off-drive. Following-on, the back of the bottle claims that this is an ale to 'quench the thirst of even the mightiest batsmen'. Bottling of Hop & Glory (like the aforementioned Porter) is carried out for the brewery by Forest Bottling of Gloucestershire. Serving recommendations are the same as for Penguin Porter.

Tasting Notes

A sweet and pleasantly fruity, orange gold beer with a hint of liquorice. Hops emerge to provide crispness and bitterness. The nose is fruity and hoppy; the finish is of hops and bitter fruit. A little low in condition but easy drinking and deceptively strong. Fine sediment.

Availability

From local Sainsbury, Tesco, Waitrose, Co-op, Bottoms Up, Greenall Cellars, Firkin off-licences, smaller off-licences and The Beer Cellar (mail order).

The Independents

Ballard's

Ballard's Brewery Ltd., Unit C, The Old Sawmill, Nyewood, Petersfield, Hampshire
GU31 5HA. Tel. (01730) 821301/821362 Fax (01730) 821742

Founded in 1980 at Cumbers Farm, Trotton, Ballard's has been trading at Nyewood
in West Sussex since 1988.

Wassail

ABV 6%   **Bottle size 500 ml**
Serve at 13° C or, alternatively, mulled in winter

Ingredients   **Pipkin pale and crystal malts; Fuggle and Golding hops**

Closely modelled on the draught version of Wassail, this bottled beer follows the same recipe and first appeared at Christmas 1995. It's now brewed every two months or so. The tall, narrow bottle is rather elegantly screen-printed rather than paper-labelled, though is a little short of detail (in other words, the bare essentials of keeping and pouring are there but the fanfares are kept to a minimum). The only words of self-aggrandisement come in the phrase 'a special strong ale' centred on the front image. Considering the care the brewery purports to take over bottling, this must be selling the beer short. It is conditioned for a week before it is brought anywhere near a bottle and then filtered, re-seeded with dried yeast and primed with sugar, before filling. Thereafter, three weeks pass before the beer is deemed to be worthy of leaving the brewery, the declared aim of this whole procedure being to produce a stable beer with a reliable shelf-life of six months (the best before date). But, for ideal results, the brewery advises a three-month drinking up period, allowing the beer twenty-four hours at room temperature before finally chilling and drinking. Keep the yeast out of the glass, or the saucepan (if you fancy the adventurous 'mulled' approach), and, with the sediment being on the loose side, choose a vessel large enough to take the bottle at one careful pour. Ballard's suggest taking a glass with strong meats like game or beef, or splash some into your casserole.

Tasting Notes

A pronounced aroma of raspberries and vanilla leads into a fruity, fairly sharp-tasting, red/brown beer with raspberry flavour giving way to a dominating, dry bitterness. Dry, bitter fruit finish. Very good drinking condition; loose sediment.

Availability

From local Tesco and Budgens, Firkin off-licences and smaller off-licences.

Old Pecker

ABV 9.7%   **Bottle size 275 ml**
Serve at 13°C or, alternatively, mulled in winter

**Ingredients Pipkin pale, crystal and chocolate malts; Fuggle and
Phoenix hops**

Old Pecker is Ballard's 1997 'year beer'. This novel approach to brewing – matching
the original gravity or alcohol by volume percentage to the last two digits of the year
in which it is brewed – is now becoming popular with a number of producers, but
Ballard's entered the fray back in 1988 with an 8.8% beer called Old Bounder. The first
of the batch rolls out on the first Sunday in December and the brew is then repeated
as required throughout the next twelve months. There is a companion draught version, too (available over Christmas and New Year), which is aged for at least two
months before dispatch to the pub. This bottled version, however, enjoys a mere week
of conditioning before being filtered, re-seeded with dried yeast, primed with sugar and
bottled, but it does, according to the brewery, have a minimum of twelve months
thereafter to reach the peak of condition. Old Pecker, complete with a screen-printed label showing a scrawny bird which has bent its beak on the head of a crusty looking old codger, is a barley wine which Ballard's suggest may be compared to ales from
the Belgian Trappist school. Store cool, as usual, but bring back to room temperature
for a day before serving, then lightly chill and pour, leaving the sediment in the bottle.
Enjoy it with beef, game or cheese or add a little (or a lot) to a Christmas pudding or
a rich fruit cake.

Tasting Notes

A dark, ruby-red beer. The heady aroma of dark fruits, hops and a
touch of vanilla – as intense as a glass of Cognac – is intoxicating in
itself. The slightly syrupy taste is very full, sweet and fruity (everything from oranges and raisins to green bananas), with a good hop
balance and some liquorice flavour. The gum-tingling finish is warm,
mostly sweetish and fruity, but at the same time is dry and balanced
by hops. Excellent drinking condition; light loose sediment.

Availability

From local Budgens and small off-licences.

The Independents

Blackawton

Blackawton Brewery, Washbourne, Totnes, Devon TQ9 7UF. Tel. (01803) 732339
Fax (01803) 732151

This small brewery was founded in 1977 and is the oldest operative brewery in Devon.

Devon Gold Export

ABV 5%	Bottle size 500 ml	Serve at 13° C

Ingredients   Pipkin pale and crystal malts; Styrian Golding hops

As its name suggests, this beer is a slightly stronger version of a cask ale called Devon Gold. Introduced in bottled form in early 1997, it is shipped in casks to Forest Bottling in Gloucestershire where packaging takes place, the beer remaining unfiltered and unprimed. The best before date is set at six months after bottling, but how well the beer survives or improves beyond this time it's too early to say.

Tasting notes

**A golden beer with malt, hops and fruit in the nose before a sharp, citric, dry and lemon taste and a dry, bitter finish.
Good drinking condition; light loose sediment.**

Availability

From Tucker's Maltings in Newton Abbot (including by mail order, tel. (01626) 334734).

Borve

Borve Brew House, Ruthven, Huntly, Moray AB54 4SR. Tel. (01466) 760343

Borve was established in 1983 on the Isle of Lewis, but moved five years later, taking up residence in a former school on the mainland. The school is now a pub, with the brewhouse adjacent.

BORVE ALE

AIR a GHRÙDAIREACHD

ANN AN EILEAN LEODHAIS

Borve Ale

ABV 4%	Bottle size 330 ml	Serve at 10°C

Ingredients   Pale, crystal and chocolate malts; roast barley;
Target hops

The brewery's original beer, Borve Ale was first presented to Scots drinkers in June 1983 as a cask ale. This bottled version (like all Borve's bottled beers) is virtually identical to the draught product, the only difference being that the bottled beers are coarse filtered (to leave some yeast in suspension) rather than fined. There are no primings and all bottled beers are part-matured on site before shipping. This particular bevvy is described by the brewery as a traditional dark, full-bodied Scotch Ale and is proudly declared to be brewed according to the German Reinheitsgebot beer purity law of 1516 (in other words, no cereals other than barley, and no adjuncts, are used). Borve recommend serving their bottled ales at 10° C, which is certainly on the cool side, but are far from adamant about this and suggest that the drinker finds his or her own preferred temperature. Storage is another matter, however, with an almost balmy (in comparison) 15° C the prescribed maximum, even a little higher for a while to get the yeast to work. Such care should enable the beers to be enjoyed 'indefinitely', although the sell by date is deliberately pitched at three–four months post-bottling to encourage shops to keep stock moving and to prevent bottles gathering dust on the shelf. All the beers come in 330 ml bottles, but the eagle-eyed may occasionally spot a 550.

Tasting Notes

**A mid-dark brown beer with good malt and hop character
(brewery's own notes – no sample supplied).**

Availability
From local small off-licences, plus mail order direct from the brewery.

Tall Ships

ABV 5%	Bottle size 330 ml	Serve at 10° C

Ingredients Pale, crystal and chocolate malts;
Target and Hersbrücker hops

This beer was first produced in August 1991 to welcome competitors in the Tall Ships Race on their arrival into Aberdeen. A case or two of this hearty brew aboard may well have trimmed their speed but would have worked wonders for their spirit on the high seas to follow, as it is brewed in the style of a real India Pale Ale, which traditionally enjoyed a robust body and a sackful of hops to keep it fresh on the way to the subcontinent. Store and serve as for Borve Ale.

Tasting Notes

**A pale-coloured, robust beer
(brewery's own notes – no sample supplied).**

Availability

From local small off-licences, plus mail order direct from the brewery.

Union Street 200

ABV 5%	Bottle size 330 ml	Serve at 10°C

Ingredients Pale malt; roast barley; Target and Hersbrücker hops

'One for the road': Union Street 200 came into existence recently as an ale commissioned by Aberdeen City Council to commemorate 200 years of its main thoroughfare. Storage and serving directions are as for Borve Ale.

Tasting Notes

**A dark, fruity, strong ale
(brewery's own notes – no sample supplied)**

Availability

From local small off-licences, plus mail order direct from the brewery.

Borve Extra Strong

ABV 10%   **Bottle size 330 ml**   **Serve at 10° C**

Ingredients   Pale and crystal malts; Target and Hersbrücker hops

At 10%, 'Extra Strong' seems rather an understatement for this unusual 'wee heavy'. What adds to its headiness is the use of American oak Bourbon casks which were previously used to mature Scotch whisky, and this oak-whisky combination imparts an unusual character. The brew first appeared in 1984, before the Bourbon casks were installed. In those days, ordinary casks filled with oak chips acted as maturation vessels. All this comes after a traditional brewing process beginning with a wort at 1085 OG. When this is fermented out, the resultant ABV, though declared here at 10%, may in fact fluctuate between 9.5 and 11%. The brewery recommends the beer be served and stored as for Borve Ale, but one would have thought something warmer than 10° C would bring better results.

Tasting Notes

A deep copper–ruby-coloured, potent ale with a smoky character (brewery's own notes – no sample supplied).

Availability
From local small off-licences, plus mail order direct from the brewery.

The Independents

Brakspear

WH Brakspear & Sons PLC, The Brewery, New Street, Henley-on-Thames, Oxfordshire RG9 2BU. Tel. (01491) 570200 Fax (01491) 410254

This classic southern brewery has its origins in the 17th-century, with the Brakspear family taking an interest from 1799. Bottling has been high on the company's agenda recently and the Christmas Ale described overleaf is planned as a forerunner of various other bottle-conditioned products.

Christmas Ale

ABV 6.5%	Bottle size 500 ml	Serve at 13° C

Ingredients Maris Otter pale, crystal and black malts; invert sugar; Fuggle, East Kent Golding and Styrian Golding hops

A welcome addition to the bottle-conditioning scene, Brakspear Christmas Ale arrived in 1996 in an unusual, hand-filled stone bottle, topped with a swing stopper. The old company logo from the turn of the century is glazed into the heavy stonework, the impermeability of which helps keep the beer cool even in less than perfect cellar conditions. The beer is dry hopped with Goldings in the conditioning tank, and the beer is racked free of sediment before bottling. The same yeast used in primary fermentation is put back into the bottle but no priming sugars are used. This is a beer which needs to mature. Brewing takes place once a year in December and six months' storage is advised, resulting in the ale coming into its own sometime after July and really finding its niche the following Christmas (a bottle I tried expressly forbade me to drink it before March 1 1997). A Belgian style chalice is the recommended glassware.

Tasting Notes

Bitter, malty and toffeeish in the Brakspear style, this ruddy-brown beer is not as sweet as expected and is very full-flavoured. The aroma is equally powerful, with malt, fruit and toffee the main characteristics. Bitter malt, hops and toffee dominate the warming finish. Soft and a little flat on the tongue; no obvious sediment.

Availability

Only from the on-site brewery shop – telephone (01491) 573242; also by mail order, 'naked' or gift packaged. Credit cards are accepted.

Burntisland

Burntisland Brewing Co., Burntisland Brewery, 83 High Street, Burntisland, Fife KY3 9AA. Tel./Fax (01592) 873333

This brewery is housed behind a delicatessen and off-licence and it only began operation in 1996.

BURNTISLAND BREWERY

Alexander's Downfall

ABV 4.3%	Bottle size 500 ml	Serve at 12° C

Ingredients   Pale and crystal malts; Fuggle and Golding hops

The Alexander donating his name to this brew is King Alexander III of Scotland who fell off his horse and died about half-a-mile from the site of Burntisland Brewery in 1286. Though some of Burntisland's cask beers (including versions of these beers) have been contract-brewed at Harviestoun Brewery, this and Dockyard Rivets opposite are both only brewed on site. They are cask-conditioned and fined before bottling but are not primed or re-seeded with yeast. The beers are also bottled here, although bottling may soon be contracted out, too. A short, two-month best before date is marked on the labels but, with the currently limited supplies, the beers usually sell out within this time.

Tasting notes

A dark golden beer with a zesty, fruit jelly-like nose. Orange fruit and bitterness fill the mouth before a dry, bittersweet finish. Lowish condition; very little yeast present.

Availability

From the brewery (including by mail order).

Dockyard Rivets

ABV 5.1%	Bottle size 500 ml	Serve at 10° C

Ingredients   Lager malt; wheat malt; Saaz hops

For the uninitiated, 'Dockyard Rivets' is a slang term referring to two parts of the body which elongate in cold weather. The name also has local relevance in that Burntisland, on the Firth of Forth, is in a dockyard/shipbuilding area and is not far from the Rosyth naval base.

Tasting notes

A smooth, malty, golden beer with good hop character, finishing bitter. The aroma is of toffeeish malt and resiny hop. Low condition; very little yeast present.

Availability
From the brewery (including by mail order).

The Independents

Burton Bridge

Burton Bridge Brewery, 24 Bridge Street, Burton upon Trent, Staffordshire DE14 1SY.
Tel. (01283) 510573 Fax (01283) 515594

Burton Bridge Brewery, the microbrewery in the pale ale capital, was established in 1982.

Burton Porter

| ABV 4.5% | Bottle size 500 ml | Serve at 13°C |

Ingredients Pipkin pale, crystal and chocolate malts; Challenger and Target hops

Simplicity is the hallmark of this award-winning beer. The name isn't fancy (it just describes the style and the place of origin) and the labelling is even more elementary. Dating back to the beer's infancy in 1983, the technique of marking the bottles for sale has not changed one bit. All that is required is a heavy hand with some yellow paint and a couple of rubber stamps and, voilà, one finished bottle. This crude approach has become the beer's trademark and the brewery is now loathe to change things. Inside the bottle is the same beer as the draught Burton Porter, filled from one-week-old casks, and it is said to be on form at any stage from one- to six-months old (the period indicated by the best before date on the front).

Tasting Notes

A dark red, almost black, porter. The aroma is of fruit and chocolate. Dry, roast malt in the taste is backed by gentle, sweet malt, with dryness, roast malt and bitterness coming through to dominate the finish. Good drinking condition.

Availability

From Burton Bridge pubs (The Burton Bridge Inn and The Alfred in Burton), plus The Bottle Store off-licence in Leicester.

Empire Pale Ale

ABV 7.5%   **Bottle size 330/500 ml**   **Serve at 13°C**

Ingredients   Pipkin pale malt; Challenger hops

As its name suggests, this brew is a re-creation of the classic IPAs which once sailed out to the far corners of the Empire from Burton upon Trent. Being very strong, bitter and hoppy, it fits the bill admirably. The days of the Raj are recalled on the label, too, which concentrates on a colourful imperial image of the old, upper-class Englishman abroad, leaving all the wording (sic) to the neck wrap. It is the back of the bottle which explains the relevance of the beer. The first brew arrived in September 1996 but the ale is only brewed to demand. After primary fermentation, it is conditioned in cask for two months and is dry-hopped for the last two weeks before being primed and bottled. The yeast carried over from the cask takes care of the bottle fermentation.

Tasting Notes

Bitter oranges are the main characteristic of this heady, copper-coloured IPA. They feature in the nose, alongside hops; they are prominent in the taste, again with powerful hops on the side; and carry right through to the warming, mouth-tingling finish. This full-bodied beer certainly tastes its strength and, although rather lively on pouring, settles down to a pleasant softness on the tongue. Fine, loose sediment.

Availability

From The Beer Cellar (mail order), plus The Bottle Store off-licence in Leicester.

Tickle Brain

ABV 8%   **Bottle size** 330/500 ml   **Serve at** 13° C

Ingredients   **Pipkin pale, crystal and chocolate malts; invert sugar; Northdown hops**

At 8%, this beer more than tickles the brain. However, the brewery gives credit for this euphemism to William Shakespeare, from whose writings the name is derived. No one can fault Burton Bridge's adventure here. Their ale is intended as an interpretation of an early (16th-century) hopped beer, as might have been produced by brewer monks. To emphasise the era it comes from (at least in spirit), King Henry VIII dominates the front label, which is wordless like that of Empire Pale Ale. The result of the brewery's experimentation is a beer in the Abbey style which will keep for up to a year after bottling (according to the best before date), but is best drunk about two months into its shelf life. Conditioning at the brewery is as for Empire Pale Ale, but without the dry hopping.

Tasting Notes

A very dark red beer with a rich, sweet, slightly sharp aroma of red berry fruits. The taste is sweetish, very fruity (red berries again), with good bitterness to beat off any threat of it becoming cloying. The finish is fruity and bitter. Very lively but good drinking condition; fairly heavy, mostly loose sediment.

Availability

From The Beer Cellar (mail order), plus The Bottle Store off-licence in Leicester.

The Independents

Butterknowle

Butterknowle Brewery, The Old School House, Lynesack, Butterknowle, Bishop Auckland, Co. Durham DL13 5QF. Tel. (01388) 710109 Fax (01388) 710373

Butterknowle Brewery was founded in 1990 and is situated in Victorian buildings, once home to the Lynesack National School.

Conciliation Ale

ABV 4.3%	Bottle size 500 ml	Serve at 13° C

Ingredients	Maris Otter pale, crystal and pale chocolate malts; Challenger hops

This bottled version of an acclaimed cask ale is now brewed every week. It's the same brew as the cask beer, except for being filtered and re-seeded with yeast (the same as used for primary fermentation), and for being primed with sugar prior to bottling. You can drink it at the 13° C suggested above, or however you like it, according to brewer John Constable, but, if you're planning to keep some for later, drink it within nine months (the best before recommendation). All brewing and bottling is done in house.

Tasting Notes

A mid-brown-coloured ale with a hoppy taste and aroma (brewery's own notes – no sample supplied).

Availability

From Oddbins, local Tesco, Asda, Co-op, smaller supermarkets and off-licences, or by mail order from the brewery.

High Force

ABV 6.2%	Bottle size 500 ml	Serve at 13° C

Ingredients Maris Otter pale and crystal malts; Challenger hops

Another cask beer put into bottle (via the same process described for Conciliation Ale), High Force is now brewed at least twice a month. It takes its name from the local High Force waterfall, but don't confuse it with beers from the neighbouring High Force Brewery. Store and serve as for Conciliation Ale.

Tasting Notes

A full-flavoured, orange-gold beer with a rich hoppy nose. In the mouth it is smooth, sweetish and fruity, yet hoppy, too, with a tangy bitter fruit finish. Excellent drinking condition; sticky sediment.

Availability
From Oddbins, local Asda, Co-op, smaller supermarkets and off-licences, or by mail order from the brewery.

The Independents

Caledonian

The Caledonian Brewing Company Ltd., 42 Slateford Road, Edinburgh EH11 1PH.
Tel. (0131) 337 1286 Fax (0131) 313 2370

The former Lorimer & Clark brewery, founded in 1869, which was taken over by Vaux
in 1919, became Caledonian in 1987 following a management buyout. It uses the last
direct-fired open coppers in the UK. The brewery produces several bottled beers but,
at present, only one is bottle-conditioned.

Tempus Fugit

ABV 4.4%	Bottle size 500 ml	Serve at 12°C

Ingredients	Pipkin pale, crystal, amber and chocolate malts; wheat malt; Fuggle and Golding hops

First brewed in May 1997 to celebrate the tenth anniversary of Caledonian, this beer is at present only available in summer, but it may soon be produced at other times of the year, too. The ten years of brewery independence have no doubt flown by for all concerned but the 'time flies' name owes more to Kensington than Edinburgh. For it was during a shopping trip to Harrods that MD Russell Sharp spotted the motto adorning the face of an antique clock. The beer itself is actually a stronger, slightly richer version of the brewery's award-winning 80/- and is bottled for Caledonian by Marston's. The beer is fermented for seven days then tanked to Burton upon Trent where Marston's condition it, filter it, re-seed it with new yeast and prime it with sugar if necessary. A six-month best before date is stamped on the label.

Tasting notes

An amber-coloured, fruity but crisp, hoppy and dry beer with a dry bitter fruit finish and hint of chocolate. Fruit and malt are strong on the nose, with some hop. Good drinking condition; very sticky sediment.

Availability
From Tesco and Oddbins.

The Independents

Chiltern

The Chiltern Brewery, Nash Lee Road, Terrick, Aylesbury, Buckinghamshire HP17 0TQ. Tel. (01296) 613647 Fax (01296) 612419

Chiltern Brewery was set up in 1980 on a small farm and specialises in beer-related foods, as well as traditional ales. On site is a well-stocked visitors' centre-cum-shop.

Bodgers Barley Wine

ABV 8.5%   **Bottle size 275 ml**   **Serve at 12-13°C**

Ingredients   **Maris Otter pale malt; Fuggle, Golding and Challenger hops**

Brewed first in 1990, to commemorate the tenth anniversary of the founding of Chiltern Brewery, Bodgers recalls the tradition of the Chiltern Bodger (a local crafts-man-chairmaker) in its name, and the year of the brewery's foundation in its original gravity (1080). It is occasionally made available on draught but otherwise is bottled as a fine accompaniment to the Chiltern range of beer-related foods. The brewery particularly recommends it with powerful cheeses, full-flavoured sausages and strong meats. The potent beer is brewed here at Chiltern but bottled elsewhere under contract. It is fined rather than filtered and is not primed with new yeast or sugar. The bottles (all individually numbered) are kept at the brewery to mature for four weeks and are then released for ideal consumption (if you follow the best before date) sometime within the next twelve months. However, the brewery has evidence that the beer lasts much longer, and some of the earliest bottles are still in prime order.

Tasting Notes

An unusual, dark gold beer, resembling a strong white wine in taste, thanks to its very fruity, dry and quite sweet characteristics. The nose is also a novelty, combining sweet malt with a resiny aroma. Mellow fruit and some hop bitterness merge in the warm, tingling finish. Excellent drinking condition; very fine loose sediment.

Availability
From the brewery shop.

The Independents

Cottage

Cottage Brewing Company, The Old Cheese Dairy, Lovington, Castle Cary, Somerset BA7 7PS. Tel. (01963) 240551 Fax (01963) 240383

Cottage Brewery was founded in 1993 and received an early boost when its draught strong ale, Norman's Conquest, claimed the *Champion Beer of Britain* title at the 1995 Great British Beer Festival.

Norman's Conquest

ABV 7%	Bottle size 330 ml	Serve at 15° C

Ingredients   Pale, crystal and chocolate malts; Challenger hops

Capitalising on the success of the brewery's award-winning cask version, bottle-conditioned Norman's Conquest was introduced in November 1995. Whilst no one can blame the brewery for boasting about its remarkable achievement in gaining CAMRA's supreme award, the wording on this bottle is, shall we say, more than a little misleading. For nowhere does it state that it was the cask version which was the *Champion Beer of Britain* and not this bottled version. This is all the more relevant when you consider that, unlike the cask brew, it is not produced by Cottage themselves but brewed (weekly) and bottled under contract by Thomas Hardy Brewery in Dorchester, albeit with Cottage-supplied ingredients and to Cottage's recipe. The brew's name is taken from the brewery owner, Chris Norman, and has a fitting original gravity of 1066. Like its cask brother, this nicely packaged bottle has been a resounding success, finding shelf space in several major stockists and helping to lead the bottle-conditioned beer revival. Whilst the beer is too new for Cottage to assess its longevity in the bottle, it certainly keeps well for up to two years and is said to improve over that time. Try it with a curry, the brewery suggests, or take your time over sips from a brandy balloon.

Tasting Notes

A full and fruity, vinous aroma leads into a strong-tasting, dark ruby-red beer with elements of red berry fruits and hop bitterness in the taste. The bitter finish has fruity malt behind and is warming. Good drinking condition; fine loose sediment.

Availability

From Tesco, Sainsbury, Asda, Waitrose, Morrison's, Co-op and Fortnum & Masons, or by mail order from the brewery.

Cropton

Cropton Brewery Co., The New Inn, Cropton, near Pickering, N. Yorkshire YO18
8HH. Tel./Fax (01751) 417310

Cropton Brewery was set up in 1984 in the cellar of the New Inn just to supply that
pub. By 1994 it had outgrown the cellar and a purpose-built brewery was installed
behind the pub.

Two Pints Bitter

ABV 4%	Bottle size 500 ml	Serve at 12° C

Ingredients **Pale and crystal malts;**
Challenger and East Kent Golding hops

A pint of Two Pints was first served at the New Inn back in the brewery's first oper-ating year of 1984 but the beer did not find its way into a bottle until December 1996. It's now brewed weekly and is the same product as the cask beer except that the beer is matured in conditioning tanks, filtered and then re-seeded with fresh yeast before filling. The label, showing a brawny chap with the appropriate two tankards in hand, carries a best before date of six months post-bottling, and Cropton advise drinking it up within this time for maximum enjoyment.

Tasting Notes

A dry, orange-brown-coloured bitter with orange fruitiness and bit-terness the key elements in the taste, preceded by a hoppy, malty nose. Dry, bitter-hop finish. Good condition; mostly sticky sediment.

Availability
From the brewery, including by mail order. Overseas orders are taken and credit cards are accepted.

Scoresby Stout

ABV 4.2%	Bottle size 500 ml	Serve at 12° C

Ingredients	Pale, roasted and crystal malts; Challenger and Golding hops

Brewed once a fortnight, this rich, dark stout takes its name from the late William Scoresby, a whaling captain who hailed from Cropton. Presumably, therefore, the ship depicted on the label is a whaler. The cask version made its debut in 1988 and this bottled variant (brewed to the same recipe but prepared for bottling in the same way as Two Pints) emerged in 1996. Also like Two Pints, this beer is best drunk within the six-month best before period.

Tasting Notes

This almost black beer (with just a hint of red colour) has a strong coffee aroma, backed by a touch of malt sweetness. In the taste, heavily roasted (almost burnt) grain presides over gentle malt sweetness and bitter hops. Bitter coffee finish. Good drinking condition.

Availability

From the brewery, including by mail order. Overseas orders are taken and credit cards are accepted.

Uncle Sams Bitter

ABV 4.4%	Bottle size	500 ml	Serve at 12° C

Ingredients   Pale malt; Cascade hops

Certainly the most distinctive of Cropton's bottled ales, Uncle Sams is a homage to the American microbrewer revolution and is chock-full of the perfumed aroma and taste of American Cascade hops. Lest there be any doubt about its inspiration, a mortar-boarded George Washington provides the focal point of the beer's label. Both this bottled and the original cask version were introduced in 1996, the only difference between the two being the pre-bottling procedure described in the earlier entry for Two Pints. Drink within the six months best before period for ideal results.

Tasting Notes

A heavily aromatic, dark golden beer. The nose is filled with sweet malt and earthy, perfumed hops which spill over into the taste to overshadow orange fruit. The finish is dry and bitter but again features scented hops. Good condition; mostly sticky sediment.

Availability

From the brewery, including by mail order. Overseas orders are taken and credit cards are accepted.

Backwoods Bitter

ABV 5.1%	Bottle size 500 ml	Serve at 12° C

Ingredients	Pale, roasted and crystal malts; Challenger and Styrian Golding hops

Where Backwoods led the other beers followed: this was the first of Cropton's ales to be bottled. That was in autumn 1995, shortly after the original cask version was first brewed, and the beer is now produced on a weekly basis. Preparation for bottling is as for the other beers, and the same guidelines for drinking up the beer apply.

Tasting Notes

Rich orange fruit takes over the aroma of this orange-brown, strong bitter. The same fruitiness is immediate in the taste before being tempered by sharp hop bitterness which continues into the after-taste and lasts and lasts. A little lively but not too heavily conditioned; sticky sediment.

Availability

From the brewery, including by mail order. Overseas orders are taken and credit cards are accepted.

The Independents

Freeminer

Freeminer Brewery Ltd, The Laurels, Sling, Coleford, Gloucestershire GL16 8JJ.
Tel./Fax (01594) 810408

Established in 1992, Freeminer is the only brewery in the Royal Forest of Dean and recalls the area's mining heritage in many of its beer names.

Freeminer Bitter

ABV 4%   **Bottle size 500 ml**   **Serve at 10° C**

**Ingredients Maris Otter pale and crystal malts;
Golding and Fuggle hops**

Like all Freeminer bottled beers, this, their benchmark bitter, is simply treated. Each is
merely filled direct from the cask by neighbouring Forest Bottling; there is no priming
of sugars and the yeast which works in the bottle is the yeast which remains in the
beer after primary fermentation. Freeminer are bullish about their beers and, judging
from the acclaim they have received in the media, rightly so. This one they describe as
a 'no-nonsense beer for drinkers who appreciate beer with taste', a pointer to the distinctively heavy hopping Freeminer beers enjoy. Each beer, as per legislation, carries
best before marks on its label, but brewery founder Don Burgess sees no reason to
stop drinking when the time is up. He also recommends you rinse the glass with cold
water immediately before serving, in the continental tradition, the purpose being to
reduce fobbing if the beer is too lively. All the beers (which are also available in cask
form) should be served yeast-free, with the exception of Shakemantle Ginger Ale (see
entry).

Tasting Notes

**An orange/gold beer with a biscuity malt nose, followed by a nicely
balanced taste of soft malt and increasingly aggressive, clean hop bitterness. The hoppy and bitter finish lasts well. Excellent condition;
fine, loose sediment.**

Availability

From Waitrose, local Tesco, local Thresher, Firkin off-licences and The Beer Cellar
(mail order).

Speculation Ale

ABV 4.7%	Bottle size 500 m	Serve at 10° C

Ingredients	Maris Otter pale, crystal and chocolate malts; Fuggle and Golding hops

Well-appreciated by *Decanter* magazine, which awarded it five stars, Speculation Ale is a premium strength bitter with a smoky character. See Freeminer Bitter for bottling information.

Tasting Notes

A full-flavoured orange/brown beer with an initial taste of fruit and malt which is quickly overwhelmed by powerful hoppy bitterness which continues into the finish. Fruit and malt on the nose. Very lively condition; heavy, loose sediment.

Availability

From Bottoms Up, Firkin off-licences and The Beer Cellar (mail order).

Shakemantle Ginger Ale

ABV 5%	Bottle size 500 ml	Serve at 10° C

Ingredients   Maris Otter pale malt; ginger; Golding hops

This is the joker in the Freeminer pack and by that I am not being unkind but merely pointing out its maverick nature. From a conventional cask beer base, the brewery develops this ale by stealing methods from traditional ginger beer production, flavouring the drink only with real ginger and forgoing artificial additives and extracts. They advise serving it cloudy, in the fashion of a wheat beer, with a little fresh lemon added to the glass. Freeminer are the first to admit that this beer will not suit every drinker but are pleased to show how keen they are to cater for minority tastes.

Tasting Notes

A cloudy, yellow/gold beer with a pronounced ginger beer and lemon aroma. The ginger is more subtle on the palate, just lurking warmly in the background behind a dry, lemony, refreshingly sharp taste. The finish, too, is sharp, dry and lemony with the ginger coming through softly, rather than aggressively. Very lively, but excellent drinking condition.

Availability

Contact Wessex Brewers on (01225) 862666 for latest stockists.

Trafalgar IPA

ABV 6%	Bottle size 500 ml	Serve at 10° C

Ingredients   Maris Otter pale and crystal malts; Golding hops

The heavy hop character of this potent brew recalls the days of the British Empire when strong, hoppy IPAs were stashed aboard sailing ships for the long journey to the Indian subcontinent. Trafalgar IPA is reputedly based on a recipe for a 9% beer but the restraints of excise duties prohibit a small producer from following this recipe to the letter (cue demands for sliding scale excise payments to aid small brewers). As if there weren't enough hops in the brew to start with, Freeminer also dry hops to embellish the nose and finish. This clearly impressed judges at the 1997 *Beauty of Hops* awards who accorded the beer the title of *Best Bottled Single Varietal.*

Tasting Notes

A pale-coloured bitter in which the dry hopping is very evident in the nose and finish (brewery's own notes – no sample supplied).

Availability

Contact Wessex Brewers on (01225) 862666 for latest stockists.

Deep Shaft Stout

ABV 6.2%	Bottle size 500 ml	Serve at 10° C

Ingredients   Maris Otter pale malt; wheat malt; roast barley; malted oats; Fuggle hops

'Not for wimps' says brewer Don Burgess. Deep Shaft is a powerful, flavoursome stout with a very dark hue, recommended to foodies in particular as an accompaniment to a sweet pudding. However, its best recommendation to date is the award of *Bottle-Conditioned Beer* of 1996 by *The Guardian* newspaper. Like the other Freeminer bottled beers, this one will improve with age. Don is currently enjoying three-year-old stocks and looking forward to further maturation.

Tasting Notes

Coffee is the predominant characteristic of this uncompromising beer, right through from its black coffee colouring. It features (with some malty sweetness and citric hop) in the aroma and dominates the long, dry finish, with bitterness and some liquorice biting away in the background. In-between, the taste mixes dark fruits with bitterness and coffeeish, roast grain flavours. Good drinking condition; loose sediment.

Availability

From Bottoms Up, Firkin off-licences and The Beer Cellar (mail order).

Frog Island

Frog Island Brewery, The Maltings, Westbridge, St James Road, Northampton NN4 8DU. Tel. (01604) 587772

Taking its name from an area of Northampton which is prone to flooding, Frog Island hopped into the brewing world in 1994, setting up shop in an old malthouse once owned by the defunct Thomas Manning brewery.

Croak & Stagger

ABV 5.6%	Bottle size 500 ml	Serve at 13° C

Ingredients	Maris Otter pale, crystal and chocolate malts; wheat malt; Target and Cascade hops

Bottled on site, unprimed, direct from the conditioning tank, Croak & Stagger is Frog Island's sole foray into the bottled beer world. It is a variation on the theme of a cask beer of the same name which was first brewed in November 1995. Brewers Bruce Littler and Graham Cherry toned down the ABV (to provide a little less Croak and a smaller chance of a Stagger) and began bottling in November 1996. Though a dark winter ale by definition, it is now made available all year round and can be ordered with personalised labels for celebrations, weddings, corporate events et al. The best before date tells you to consume it within eleven months, but it's ready to drink, say the brewers, as soon as it leaves the brewery.

Tasting Notes

A strong, dark brown beer with a honey/fruit nose, backed by roast malt. Bitter chocolate and malty sweetness follow in the taste, and there is a gentle bittersweet finish (brewery's own notes – no sample supplied).

Availability

From pubs selling Frog Island cask beers and local farm shops. A mail order service may soon be available from the brewery.

The Independents

Fuller's

Fuller, Smith and Turner PLC, Griffin Brewery, Chiswick Lane South, Chiswick, London W4 2QB. Tel. (0181) 996 2000 Fax (0181) 995 0230

One of the capital's two major brewers, Fuller's operates on a site linked to beer production for over 325 years. Messers Fuller, Smith and Turner came together in 1845 and descendants of the founders are still on the board today.

1845 Celebration Ale

ABV 6.3%	Bottle size 500 ml	Serve at 12° C

Ingredients Pale, crystal, brown and chocolate malts; Golding hops

This is Fuller's only bottle-conditioned beer and there is no cask equivalent. It was first brewed in February 1995 to commemorate the 150th anniversary of the founding of the company, with the Prince of Wales doing the honours and adding the hops. Its success has meant that it is now a permanent member of the award-winning Fuller's range of traditional ales, with brews taking place monthly. After primary fermentation the beer enjoys two weeks in conditioning tanks and is then filtered, re-seeded with yeast from primary fermentation and then bottled, with no primings. Two weeks of conditioning follow before the bottles are released from the brewery. Once this two-week period has been observed, Fuller's reckon that the beer is at its best and will remain so at least up to the prescribed twelve-month best before date. Try it with meats, Fuller's suggest. The bottle itself is of Fuller's own individual, award-winning design (*Best Dressed Bottle* 1996 from the The British Bottlers' Institute).

Tasting Notes

A rich, dark amber beer with a glorious, fruity, malty nose, backed by hints of sherry and Golding hop. The very full, smooth, malty and fruity taste is quickly balanced by hop bitterness. Bitter fruit features in the lingering finish. Excellent drinking condition.

Availability

From Fuller's pubs, Tesco, Sainsbury, Asda, Waitrose, Budgens, Victoria Wine, plus cash and carry warehouses and other off-licences.

The Independents

Gale's

George Gale & Co. Ltd., The Hampshire Brewery, London Road, Horndean, Hampshire PO8 0DA. Tel. (01705) 571212 Fax (01705) 598641

Hampshire's major brewery, Gale's was founded in 1847 and is still family owned. As well as the classic Prize Old Ale listed below, Gale's also produced a commemorative bottle-conditioned beer (7.1%) for CAMRA's 25th birthday in 1996, stocks of which may still be available.

Prize Old Ale

ABV 9%	Bottle size 275 ml	Serve at Room Temperature

Ingredients	Maris Otter pale and black malts; Fuggle and Golding hops

Famous as the last British beer to be sold in a corked bottle, Prize Old Ale is fundamental to the traditional, family image of Gale's. It was introduced in the 1920s, when a new head brewer brought the recipe with him from Yorkshire. The recipe has remained largely unchanged in the subsequent 70-odd years, except for the use of pelletised hops instead of whole hops and the loss of wooden hogsheads which were used for conditioning the beer. The replacement metal tanks may not be as charming or quaint but, according to head brewer Derek Lowe, they produce more reliable beer, and it is in these containers that the beer is aged for six–twelve months. The beer is fined in the tanks after about six months and, before being bottled, more of the same original yeast may be added. Being corked, this is the one bottle-conditioned beer which should be stored lying down, to keep the cork moist, but beware: if the storage temperature is too high the cork may blow in this position. Prize Old Ale is aged for three months at the brewery before leaving the site and will continue to improve for up to at least five years thereafter (the best before date is set at four years). Some twenty-year-old bottles have been known to be excellent, but this doesn't mean that all beers of such an age will prove as fulfilling. All bottles are now individually numbered. For more about Prize Old Ale see *The Classics* at the front of this book.

Tasting Notes

(based on fairly young samples) A deep, vinous, fruity aroma with hints of vanilla precedes a powerful, mouth-filling combination of fruit (dates and raisins), bitterness and alcoholic strength. The finish is dry and not as heavy as expected, with bitter fruit and hops shading out sweetness. The condition appears very light but still makes its mark on the tongue. Dark ruby-red in colour.

Availability

From Gale's pubs, local Tesco and The Beer Cellar (mail order).

Hanby

Hanby Ales Ltd., New Brewery, Aston Park, Soulton Road, Wem, Shropshire SY4 5SD. Tel./Fax (01939) 232432

Following the closure of Wem Brewery by Greenalls in 1988, its head brewer, Jack Hanby, set up his own business. New premises were acquired in 1990.

Premium

ABV 4.6%	Bottle size 500 ml	Serve at 13° C

Ingredients	Maris Otter pale and crystal malts; Fuggle and Golding hops

Hanby's Premium is a new venture for this microbrewery. It was trialled in spring 1997 and officially launched in July the same year. It's the same brew as the company's Treacleminer cask ale, but with the name changed to ensure that buyers aren't misled into thinking it is an overly sweet ale. Hanby brew and bottle it on site, maturing the beer in conditioning tanks from which the bottles are filled without filtering or re-seeding yeast.

Tasting Notes

An amber-coloured beer with a fruity, hoppy aroma, a smooth fruity flavour and a hoppy finish (brewery's own notes – no sample supplied).

Availability

Contact the brewery for the latest stockists.

The Independents

Hardy

Thomas Hardy Brewing Ltd., Weymouth Avenue, Dorchester, Dorset DT1 1QT.
Tel. (01305) 251251 Fax (01305) 258300

Founded by the Eldridge family as the Green Dragon Brewery in 1837, this brewery now operates as the Thomas Hardy brewery, following a division of the Eldridge Pope company in 1996. It brews beers under contract for Eldridge Pope and other companies.

Thomas Hardy's Ale

ABV 12%	Bottle size 330 ml	Serve at Room Temperature

Ingredients   Pipkin pale and pale lager malts; Golding hops

An all-time bottled great (discussed in more detail in *The Classics* feature at the front of this book), Hardy's Ale was created by Eldridge Pope in 1968 and, although it is brewed by the new Thomas Hardy company, it is still officially an Eldridge Pope beer. Its inspiration was a passage in Hardy's novel *The Trumpet-Major* which described Dorchester's strong beer thus:

'It was of the most beautiful colour that the eye of an artist in beer could desire; full in body, yet brisk as a volcano; piquant, yet without a twang; luminous as an autumn sunset; free from streakiness of taste but finally, rather heady'.

This famous quote is recalled on the label of each individually numbered and dated bottle.

Tasting Notes

(1988 vintage) A dark ruby-red beer with a magnificent, sherry-like, fruity aroma with a touch of woodiness. The strong, mouth-filling sweetness is well balanced by hop bitterness and fruit (strawberries), whilst the syrupy, warming finish is again reminiscent of sherry. Lowish, but not too low, condition; loose sediment.

Availability
From Eldridge Pope pubs and The Beer Cellar (mail order).

The Independents

Harveys

Harvey & Son (Lewes) Ltd., The Bridge Wharf Brewery, 6 Cliffe High Street, Lewes, E. Sussex BN7 2AH. Tel. (01273) 480209 Fax (01273) 483706

Established in the late 18th century by John Harvey, on the banks of the River Ouse, this Georgian brewery was rebuilt in 1881 and the Victorian Gothic tower and brew-house remain a very attractive feature. Harveys is still family-run.

HARVEYS

1859 Porter

ABV 4.8%	Bottle size 275 ml	Serve at 14° C

Ingredients	Maris Otter pale, black and crystal malts; Fuggle and East Kent Golding hops

Be careful when seeking out this much acclaimed porter: a pasteurised version also exists and has now become more common, with this bottle-conditioned option now only brewed to demand. The recipe dates, as the name indicates, from the year 1859, but the beer existed only as notes in a brewing book for most of this century. In 1993 Harveys happily brought it back to life, ironically just at about the same time as Guinness were condemning their classic Original Stout to the pasteuriser. After brewing, 1859 Porter is taken directly from the fermenting vessel and racked into sterile casks (with no additions), from which the beer is bottled. Harveys ensure the bottles have at least three weeks at the brewery to mellow out, with a best before date of three months later stamped on after that. Try it, perhaps, with a plate of seafood in the old porter way. A cask version is also made available in March each year.

Tasting Notes

A black porter with a complex palate (brewery's own notes – no sample supplied).

Availability
From the brewery shop and The Beer Cellar (mail order).

The Independents

High Force

High Force Hotel Brewery, Forest-in-Teesdale, Barnard Castle, Co. Durham DL12 0XH. Tel. (01833) 622222 Fax (01833) 622264

This, the only brew pub in Co. Durham, went into production in November 1995. It claims to be the highest brewery in Britain: at 1,060 feet it is situated by the High Force waterfall in a popular tourist area.

Cauldron Snout

ABV 5.6%   **Bottle size** 480 ml   **Serve at** 12° C

Ingredients   Maris Otter pale and crystal malts; wheat malt; roast barley; Fuggle and Golding hops

Described as a strong, dark, old ale, Cauldron Snout (and its cask equivalent) is named after a waterfall in Upper Teesdale, the water from which finds its way, via Cow Green Reservoir, to the brewery. The beer is cask-conditioned on site before shipping to the Brewlab brewing services department at Sunderland University where it is checked and adjusted for yeast and sugar content before bottling. The best before date is fairly short – just four months from bottling time. Bottles are only available from the brew pub itself at this stage, but, if you make the effort to collect, pop into the local butcher's where Cauldron Snout sausages are made.

Tasting Notes

A strong, dark old ale (brewery's own notes – no sample supplied).

Availability

From the brewery.

Hogs Back

Hogs Back Brewery, Manor Farm, The Street, Tongham, Surrey GU10 1DE.
Tel. (01252) 783000 Fax (01252) 782328

This purpose-built brewery was set up in a restored farm building (circa 1768) in 1992 and the popularity of its ales has helped it to expand. It now has a well-stocked shop/off-licence on site, offering a wide range of English and foreign (particularly Belgian) bottled beers. In addition to the beers listed on the following pages, there are plans to bottle-condition the brewery's best bitter TEA (Traditional English Ale).

BSA (Burma Star Ale)

ABV 4.5%	Bottle size 275 ml	Serve at 13° C

Ingredients	Pipkin pale, crystal and chocolate malts; Fuggle and Golding hops

Introduced in 1995 to commemorate the fiftieth anniversary of VJ Day, BSA is available in cask form as well as in this bottle-conditioned version which is only produced each June or July. The beer is matured at the brewery, filtered and then injected with fresh yeast for bottle-conditioning. Bottling of this and all Hogs Back beers is contracted out to Old Luxters Brewery. The packaging is deliberately 1940sesque and has no doubt helped encourage the Imperial War Museum to take stocks for sale to its visitors. The brewery advises that the best time to drink the beer is within two to three months of bottling (the best before mark is four months). Try it with red meats, Hogs Back suggests.

Tasting Notes

An amber ale with malt and hops balanced in the aroma, a fruity flavour and a mellow, fruity finish (brewery's own notes – no sample supplied).

Availability

From the Imperial War Museum, London, major wholesalers and the brewery shop (mail order available). Overseas orders are taken and credit cards are accepted.

Brewster's Bundle

ABV 7.4%	Bottle size 275 ml	Serve at 14° C

Ingredients   **Pipkin pale and crystal malts; Fuggle and Golding hops**

Another commemorative brew, but recalling happier times than the brewery's BSA, this ale is produced and bottled each February. The 'Bundle' in question is Charley, the first baby daughter of Hogs Back's lady brewster, born in February 1994 at the weight of 7lb 4oz (hence the 7.4% ABV). If you can lay your hands on one of the gilt-lettered bottles, drink it within twelve months (as requested by the best before date) – or, even better, within six months for the strongest hoppy flavours. Fish or poultry apparently go well with this pale golden ale. Like the BSA, the beer is matured on site and filtered, but then re-seeded with yeast in preparation for bottling.

Tasting Notes

A pale golden ale with a flowery hop aroma, a full, rich, hoppy taste and a lingering hoppy finish (brewery's own notes – no sample supplied).

Availability

From local Tesco, some off-licences, major wholesalers and the brewery shop (mail order available). Overseas orders are taken and credit cards are accepted.

Wobble in a Bottle

ABV 7.5%	Bottle size 500 ml	Serve at 14° C

Ingredients	Pipkin pale, crystal and chocolate malts; Fuggle and Golding hops

Wobble in a Bottle is the bottled version of Hogs Back's Christmas beer, Santa's Wobble. It was first produced in 1996 and is now brewed every three months or so. The bottling procedure is as for the other beers from the brewery, and the bottle is presented with a gold plastic seal over the crown cap. Serve, perhaps, instead of a port at the end of a dinner, but go easy or you might end up like the befuddled old chap on the label. For best results consume within two months of bottling, and no later than a year (the best before is set between six and twelve months, depending on the nature of the batch).

Tasting Notes

An unusual, red-brown beer with a rich, raspberry-ish aroma. The taste is full, fruity and sherbety, with a refreshingly sharp edge and without the alcoholic heaviness or cloying sweetness you'd expect. Sharp bitterness dominates fruit in the finish. Good, lively condition; solid yeast sediment.

Availability

From local Tesco, some off-licences and the brewery shop (mail order available). Overseas orders are taken and credit cards are accepted.

A over T (Aromas Over Tongham)

ABV 9%	Bottle size 275 ml	Serve at 14° C

Ingredients	Pipkin pale, crystal and chocolate malts; Fuggle and Golding hops

One of Hogs Back's earliest brews, A Over T (named after its unfortunate side-effect) first tempted drinkers back in 1993, when it appeared in cask form. The bottled version conforms to the same recipe, except for the nuances of the bottling procedure described here for the brewery's other beers. Drink it within twelve months (the best before date) but try to consume within six for best results. Steak meals benefit from a glass of A Over T at your elbow, according to the brewers, and Christmas puddings come alive if dosed with this rich barley wine.

Tasting Notes

A dark ruby-coloured beer with a vinous, fruity nose, a full-bodied, almost smoky, chocolate taste and a lingering fruity finish (brewery's own notes – no sample supplied).

Availability

From local Tesco, some off-licences, major wholesalers and the brewery shop (mail order available). Overseas orders are taken and credit cards are accepted.

The Independents

Hop Back

Hop Back Brewery PLC, Unit 22–24 Batten Road Industrial Estate, Downton, Salisbury, Wiltshire SP5 3HU. Tel. (01725) 510986 Fax (01725) 513116

Originally based at a Salisbury brew pub, the Wyndham Arms, Hop Back was set up in 1987. It moved to a unit on an industrial area at Downton in 1992 and stepped up its bottled beer production in 1997 with the installation of a new bottling line.

Summer Lightning

ABV 5%	Bottle size 500 ml	Serve at 12° C

Ingredients	Maris Otter pale malt; East Kent Golding hops

The story of Summer Lightning goes back to the late 1980s. MD and brewery founder John Gilbert came up with the recipe for this pale, crisp and hoppy, yet strong, beer to contrast with the other 5% beers of the time which were nearly all dark, sweet and sickly. In cask form it's been a trend setter. Since winning the *Best New Brewery Beer* award at the *Champion Beer of Britain* contest in 1989, it has inspired brewers up and down the land to create strong but pale beers which have appeal beyond the traditional ale drinker. The bottle-conditioned version is a relatively new concept and really only began to find a niche in 1997. To enhance its appeal, Hop Back have now changed the beer into a single varietal hop brew, ditching the Challenger hops it used to include in favour of East Kent Goldings only. The draught version is not single varietal and differs in a number of respects. The bottled beer, for instance, is cold-conditioned at 3° C, kräusened to give the condition a boost (this involves adding partially fermented wort to the finished beer) and chill proofed. Probably the most notable difference to the consumer is in the carbonation level, with the bottle performing more briskly on the tongue, though the carbonation is balanced from brew to brew by adjusting the amount of yeast and fresh wort going into the bottle. Finished bottles are kept warm at the brewery for a week before shipping. The best before date is set eighteen months ahead but the brewery have no experience of older versions to be able to say how well it keeps beyond this time. To serve, pour into an oversized wet glass (to keep the lively condition under control).

Tasting Notes

A pale, easy-drinking, strong bitter, quenching but dry. The citric, hoppy and malty nose leads to a lightly fruity taste with crisp, clean hoppiness and a dry, hoppy, bitter finish. Lively condition; loose sediment.

Availability

From Hop Back pubs, Oddbins, local small supermarkets and The Beer Cellar (mail order).

Thunderstorm

| ABV 5% | Bottle size 500 ml | Serve at 12° C |

Ingredients   Maris Otter pale malt; wheat malt; Progress hops

In cask form this beer picked up the top honour at the 1996 *Beauty of Hops* contest, in the category for beers made with only Progress hops. It made its debut in bottled form in spring 1997 and follows the same recipe as the cask brew. The bottling procedure emulates that of Summer Lightning and, like the latter, it is best served in an oversized, wet glass, with the sediment left in the bottle. Try it with fish, suggests brewer Rik Lyall. Properly store bottles and they should easily survive the eighteen-month best before date.

Tasting Notes

Another dry, quenching beer which doesn't taste its strength. Aromas of pears, bread and bubblegum precede a citric, dry, hoppy taste with some fruit lurking in the background. The finish is very dry, bitter, hoppy and a little bit bready. Very lively condition; pale gold in colour.

Availability

From Hop Back pubs and local small supermarkets.

Hoskins & Oldfield

Hoskins & Oldfield Brewery Ltd., North Mills, Frog Island, Leicester LE3 5DH.
Tel. (0116) 251 0532

This brewery was established by Philip and Stephen Hoskins, following the sale of their family (Hoskins) brewery in 1984.

'O4' Ale

ABV 5.2%	Bottle size 500 ml	Serve at 13° C

Ingredients	Maris Otter pale and crystal malts; wheat malt; Northdown, Mount Hood and Bramling Cross hops

Taking its name from an LNER steam engine classification, this beer is produced to help raise funds for the restoration of an engine belonging to the National Railway Museum. The engine is housed at the Great Central Railway in Loughborough. The project is a joint initiative with *Steam Railway* magazine and 'O4' has also been sold in cask-conditioned form. The bottled beer is stored in casks before being fined, re-dosed with the same strain of yeast and filled on site by hand. Hoskins & Oldfield have dabbled in bottle-conditioned beer production in the past but they hope that this will be the first of a new range.

Tasting notes

No sample or tasting notes supplied.

Availability
From local off-licences and from the brewery (including by mail order).

The Independents

Hughes

Sarah Hughes Brewery, Beacon Hotel, 129 Bilston Street, Sedgley, Dudley,
W. Midlands DY3 1JE. Tel. (01902) 883380

After lying idle for 30 years, this Black Country brewery was re-opened in 1987 by the
grandson of the founder, Sarah Hughes. Initially serving just the village pub and a few
other local houses, it now also supplies beer to the free trade.

Dark Ruby

ABV 6%	Bottle size 275 ml	Serve at 13° C

Ingredients   **Maris Otter pale and crystal malts; Fuggle and Golding hops**

Originally brewed by Sarah Hughes back in 1921, this strong dark mild was the first brew resurrected by the brewery in 1987. This bottled version (identical to the award-winning draught beer, and simply filled from the cask with no primings) was only made available for the first time in 1995, so there's no evidence yet about how well it matures in the bottle over a length of time. Although the beer is brewed here, it is bottled off-site. Founder Sarah Hughes herself is depicted on the label.

Tasting Notes

As expected, dark ruby in colour. The aroma of sweet fruit and chocolate gives way to sweet, fruit and malt in the taste, with a light scented hop edge. Malty, dry and more bitter finish. Excellent drinking condition; loose sediment.

Availability

From various beer wholesalers, plus mail order direct from the brewery, including overseas shipping.

The Independents

King & Barnes

King & Barnes Ltd., The Horsham Brewery, 18 Bishopric, Horsham, W. Sussex RH12 1QP. Tel. (01403) 270470 Fax (01403) 270570

Dating back almost 200 years and in the present premises since 1850, this brewery is still run by the King family, who united with the Barnes family brewery in 1906. In recent years, it has pitched headlong into the bottle-conditioned beer market, leading the way with a version of its premium cask ale, Festive, and, in 1997, unveiling a high-tech new bottling line, largely dedicated to bottle-conditioned beer packaging. In addition to the beers listed below, the brewery plans a series of single varietal bottled beers, featuring Challenger and Liberty hops amongst others, plus a Rye Beer.

King & Barnes Ltd
Traditional Brewers for over a Century

Wheat Mash

ABV 4.5%	Bottle size 550 ml	Serve at 14° C

Ingredients	Lager and Carapils malts; wheat malt; Yakima County, Cluster and WGV hops

Wheat Mash began life as a draught commemorative beer, brewed to mark the 50th anniversary of VE Day in 1995. The beer is now brewed according to demand and is also sold under the name of Spring Ale, though this is primarily for exports to Sweden where the name Wheat Mash may cause confusion with their imported German wheat beers. All K&B bottled beers are prepared for the bottle in the same way as Festive Ale (see entry).

Tasting Notes

A dark golden beer with an unusual aroma of hops and pine. The flavour is very full, bittersweet and dry, with excellent hop character over a sweet, light, malty base. Very dry, lasting, bittersweet finish. Good drinking condition; mostly sticky sediment.

Availability

From the brewery shop.

Harvest Ale

ABV 4.7%   **Bottle size 550 ml**   **Serve at 14° C**

Ingredients   Pale, crystal and enzymic malts; flaked maize; Golding hops

The single varietal hop Harvest Ale is the most unusual of the K&B range, in that each brew is quite different. It is produced only once a year – at harvest time, naturally – and incorporates the very freshest ingredients, including new malted barley (still warm from the kilns) and new season green hops. Whilst the basic recipe may be the same from year to year, there's no guaranteeing what the beer will taste like because of the untried ingredients. All the same, by using a skilled maltster and 'harvesting' all their own brewing experience, the result is usually a beer to savour rather than one to swill. See Festive Ale for bottling and serving details.

Tasting Notes

(1996 vintage) A bronze-coloured beer with a light, malty nose. The flavour is full and initially sweet, balanced with the bitterness of earthy hops which gradually dominate. Hoppy bitterness presides over sweet malt in the aftertaste. Good, not too lively, condition; mostly sticky sediment.

Availability
From Oddbins and the brewery shop.

Festive Ale

ABV 5.3%	Bottle size 550 ml	Serve at 14° C

Ingredients	Pale, crystal, chocolate and enzymic malts; flaked maize; Golding, WGV and Challenger hops

The head of the class. It was the great success of Festive when trialled in Oddbins which convinced K&B to expand its bottle-conditioned beer range. The beer had been around in cask form since 1951, when it was created to commemorate the Festival of Britain. There had also been a pasteurised bottle version. After a period of non-production, it returned as a cask beer in 1981, when the company's new brewhouse was completed. The first bottle-conditioning took place in 1992, as a bit of an experiment. The brewers decided to prepare some bottles of Christmas Ale as a surprise yuletide gift for other members of staff and some found its way onto the desks at Oddbins who immediately asked for more, but with a little less potency. Festive was tried and the rest is history. Its quality was confirmed when it collected the *Best Bottle-Conditioned Beer* award at CAMRA's *Champion Beer of Britain* contest in 1995. Like all K&B bottled beers, Festive is matured after fermentation in conditioning tanks, warm-conditioned for a week and then lightly chilled (7° C) for at least one more week. It is then filtered bright and re-seeded with primary fermentation yeast before being primed with high maltose syrup. The brewery stamp a fifteen-month best before date on each bottle, but claim this could easily be a 'best after' date, so well do the beers continue to mature beyond this time.

Tasting Notes

This reddish-brown beer has a thick, foaming beige head when poured. Malt, fruit and hops are apparent in the aroma but really make their presence felt in the mouth-filling taste, the hops coming through to counter the immediate malty fruitiness. Good, moreish finish with bitter fruit and hops. Quite lively condition; sediment mostly stays at the bottom of the bottle.

Availability

From Oddbins, Waitrose, local Tesco, Sainsbury, The Beer Cellar (mail order) and the brewery shop.

Old Porter

ABV 5.5%	Bottle size 550 ml	Serve at 14° C

Ingredients	Pale, crystal and chocolate malts; wheat malt; Golding, WGV and Challenger hops

If Festive is the head of the class, Old Porter certainly merits prefect status. It quickly followed Festive onto the Oddbins shelves and has provided a benchmark for other bottled porters. Old Porter is sadly not available in cask form, but it is sold as a keg stout. It is prepared for the bottle as Festive, except that molasses are used for priming in place of high maltose syrup.

Tasting Notes

An archetypal porter, dark red/brown in colour, with a cappuccino-coloured head. It is sweet and clean tasting with coffee flavours working their way through. Good, fresh aroma of sweetness, fruitiness and roast malt; quickly drying, bittersweet coffee finish, with a hint of liquorice. Lively condition, but not too fizzy; mostly sticky sediment.

Availability
From Oddbins, Waitrose, The Beer Cellar (mail order) and the brewery shop.

Corn Beer

| ABV 6.5% | Bottle size 550 ml | Serve at 14° C |

| Ingredients | Lager and enzymic malts; corn; wheat malt; Golding, WGV and Challenger hops |

K&B are certainly not afraid to experiment. Like the forthcoming Rye Beer, Corn Beer is one of the brewery's creations featuring a high percentage of cereals other than barley malt.

Tasting Notes

A dark golden beer whose predominant characteristic is sweetness, from the aroma (which also has a hint of hop), to the warming, syrupy taste and the slightly more bitter finish. Very lively condition; some yeast in suspension.

Availability

From Oddbins, The Beer Cellar (mail order) and the brewery shop.

Christmas Ale

ABV 8%	Bottle size 330 ml	Serve at 14° C

Ingredients	Pale, crystal and enzymic malts; flaked maize; Golding, WGV and Challenger hops

The 'festive' beer, as opposed to the 'Festive' beer. K&B's Christmas Ale is derived from an old brewery recipe for Golding Barley Wine and at 8% it warrants that title. This was the beer which first stimulated Oddbins' interest in the brewery's bottles. It keeps very well – the best before date on a 1996 bottle is Christmas Day 2000 – and is, according to those who know, better at least a year after bottling than fresh, the bottle-conditioning mellowing out the sweetness and bringing forward the hop bitterness. It's only brewed once a year, and each bottle is vintage dated. One to add to your Christmas pudding mix.

Tasting Notes

A very full-flavoured, complex, dark copper-coloured beer, a touch warming. Immediately sweet-tasting, it becomes bitter with fruit, nuts, hops and hints of marzipan coming through before a fruity, mildly tingling finish which is more bitter than sweet. All this follows a malty and hoppy aroma which has sweet raisin fruit behind. Good drinking condition; sticky sediment.

Availability
From Oddbins and the brewery shop.

Millennium Ale

ABV 9.5%	Bottle size 640 ml	Serve at 12–14° C

Ingredients	Maris Otter pale malt; Golding and Early Bird Golding hops

You will note that there are no tasting notes offered for this beer. As it's meant to be consumed as the clocks tick over into the new millennium, it would be quite unfair to judge it on its current status. (Wait till the year 2000 edition of this book.) It was brewed at 6.30 am on the 4th September 1996 and, as the brewery says, it'll take at least three years for the malt and hops to come into balance. Until that time you can enjoy the anticipation and appreciate the quality packaging. Each bottle comes in a straw-lined wooden box and is wax sealed. An informative booklet is attached to the neck of the bottle, giving full details of the ingredients and the philosophy behind a millennium beer, and explaining how all the brewery staff (including the directors) all pitched in to hand-bottle the beer. As this is a one-off, limited edition brew, each bottle has an individual number. You pay for it though: bottles retail at around the £11 mark. Save up and treat yourself to something special for the big event.

Availability

From Oddbins, The Beer Cellar (mail order) and the brewery shop.

The Independents

Lakeland

The Lakeland Brewing Company, 1 Sepulchre Lane, Kendal, Cumbria LA9 4NJ.
Tel./Fax (01539) 734528

Lakeland began operations in 1990, based at the famous Masons Arms pub at Cartmel Fell. There is still a brewery there, now operating under the name of Strawberry Bank, but Lakeland has moved out. As we went to press, the brewer, Nigel Stevenson, was still looking for new brewing premises but was hiring another brewery's equipment to produce his own beers.

Amazon

ABV 4.5%	Bottle size 500 ml	Serve at 13°C

Ingredients **Pale and crystal malts; Mount Hood and Willamette hops**

Like all Lakeland's beers, Amazon takes its name from a novel by local author Arthur Ransome (in this case *Swallows and Amazons*). A boating scene from the children's book is depicted on the label. The beer is bottled by Burton Bridge from Lakeland's casks, with the beer primed if necessary but otherwise no finings, filtration or re-seeding of yeasts. The best before date is set nine months post-bottling.

Tasting notes

A fruity, bittersweet, nicely rounded, orange-gold beer with a fruity, malty nose. The finish is pleasantly bitter, dry and hoppy. Good drinking condition; loose sediment.

Availability

From local supermarkets and off-licences, plus other specialist beer shops.

Great Northern

ABV 5%	Bottle size 500 ml	Serve at 13° C

Ingredients	Pale and crystal malts; Mount Hood and Willamette hops

Lakeland was one of the first of the new small breweries to experiment with bottle-conditioning beers and Great Northern was one of its first bottled beers. Like the brewery's other ales, it features North American hops. For the bottling procedure, see Amazon.

Tasting notes

No sample or tasting notes supplied.

Availability

From local supermarkets and off-licences, plus other specialist beer shops.

Winter Holiday

ABV 5%	Bottle size 500 ml	Serve at 13°C

Ingredients	Pale, crystal and chocolate malts; Mount Hood and Willamette hops

Winter Holiday is the only one of Lakeland's bottled ales which is not also available in cask form. The use of chocolate malt also makes it a darker beer than the others. See Amazon for bottling details.

Tasting notes

No sample or tasting notes supplied.

Availability
From local supermarkets and off-licences, plus other specialist beer shops.

Big Six

| ABV 6% | Bottle size 500 ml | Serve at 13°C |

Ingredients   Pale malt; honey; Mount Hood and Willamette hops

This beer, too, is named after an Arthur Ransome book and, although it's been around for some time in cask form, it has only recently been made available in bottled form. A distinguishing feature is the use of honey to add texture and background sweetness. Again, see Amazon for bottling details.

Tasting notes

No sample or tasting notes supplied.

Availability

From local supermarkets and off-licences, plus other specialist beer shops.

Leatherbritches

Leatherbritches Brewery, Bently Brook Inn, Fenny Bentley, Ashbourne, Derbyshire DE61LF. Tel. (01335) 350278 Fax (01335) 350422

Leatherbritches Brewery is housed behind the Bently Brook Inn, just north of Ashbourne, a pub owned by the parents of brewery founder Bill Allingham. Bill has tried brewing various bottle-conditioned beers but has now settled on the two described overleaf.

Steamin' Billy Bitter

ABV 4.5%	Bottle size 500 ml	Serve at 13° C

Ingredients	Maris Otter pale and crystal malts; Progress and Goldings hops

Brewed for the Steamin' Billy company, of which Bill Allingham owns half, this bitter replaces the brewery's Belt 'n' Braces 3.8% ale in bottle form. It is actually a dry-hopped variation of Leatherbritches draught Ashbourne Ale and is simply filled from the cask by hand, with no priming sugars added. The best before date is six months after bottling, even though Bill reckons it is actually better after this time. The original Steamin' Billy was a Jack Russell dog.

Tasting Notes

A hoppy, dry bitter with a floral hop nose and a clean finish (brewery's own notes – no sample supplied).

Availability

From the brewery, the two Steamin' Billy pubs in Leicester (The Cow & Plough and The Vaults), and small off-licences.

Scrum Down Mild

| ABV 5.3% | Bottle size 500 ml | Serve at 13° C |

Ingredients   Maris Otter chocolate and crystal malts; Fuggle hops

This dark mild was introduced in bottled form in 1997 and is brewed, like Steamin' Billy Bitter, once a month or thereabouts.

Tasting Notes

A very dark beer with a malty and chocolatey aroma, a malty, sweet taste and a lingering sweet aftertaste (brewery's own notes – no sample supplied).

Availability

From the brewery, the two Steamin' Billy pubs in Leicester (The Cow & Plough and The Vaults), and small off-licences.

The Independents

Linfit

Linfit Brewery, Sair Inn, Lane Top, Linthwaite, Huddersfield, W. Yorkshire HD7 5SG.
Tel. (01484) 842370

Linfit Brewery's home is at the 19th-century Sair Inn, a brew pub which recommenced
brewing in 1982 and became CAMRA's national *Pub of the Year* in 1996.

Linfit Brewery

English Guineas

ABV 5.5%	Bottle size 500 ml	Serve at 10° C

Ingredients   **Pale malt; roast barley; Challenger hops**

Not a Johnny-come-lately. This strong, dry stout first appeared in 1984, well ahead of most of the bottle-conditioned beers in this book and, consequently, is testament to the importance of microbreweries in shaping the British beer market. With English Guineas as its name, and label typography not a million miles removed from that used by Guinness, it is easy to see where this beer gets its inspiration. As with many small brewers, the bottling procedure is elementary: the bottles are just filled from the conditioning tank and kept at the brewery until they are in condition. The six months' best before period is purely nominal as the brewery claims to have enjoyed bottles over two years-old, even if they were just a bit over-conditioned by this time.

Tasting Notes

No sample or tasting notes supplied.

Availability

From the brewery and small off-licences.

Marston's

Marston, Thompson & Evershed PLC, Shobnall Road, Burton upon Trent, Staffordshire
DE14 2BW. Tel. (01283) 531131 Fax (01283) 510378

One of Britain's best-known regional breweries, Marston's was founded in 1834 and is
the only producer still using the Burton Union system of fermentation for its draught
beers. It also produces a good range of bottled beers, although most of them are pasteurised.

Oyster Stout

ABV 4.5%	Bottle size 500 ml	Serve at 10° C

Ingredients	Maris Otter and Pipkin pale and black malts; roast barley; Fuggle and Golding hops

In 1993 Marston's introduced a new guest beer scheme for selected pub tenants. Called Head Brewer's Choice, it aimed to provide a new beer every two weeks, sourced not from outside the brewery but created by the head brewer, Paul Bayley, himself. HBC has been a great success and one of its by-products has been this acclaimed Oyster Stout. This dark brew was given an airing in cask in February 1995 and was based on a revived traditional recipe. It is now bottled every two–three weeks and, in 1996, earned itself the title of *Best Bottle-Conditioned Beer* at CAMRA's *Champion Beer of Britain* awards. The bottled beer differs from the draught in some respects, namely in its maturation in tanks prior to bottling, to allow the flavours to mellow out and the carbonation to increase. Filtered, it is then re-seeded with select- ed new yeast and is primed with sugar as and when required, depending on the resid- ual sweetness at the end of maturation. Drink in line with the best before date (six months post-bottling), with or without the yeast content. As its name suggests, it goes well with oysters and other seafood.

Tasting Notes

A dark brown/red stout with a cappuccino-coloured head. Very smooth drinking, this beer is not too heavy and is reasonably thin- bodied but does not lack flavour. Coffee is apparent in the nose, fol- lowed by a dry taste of sweet, coffeeish roast grain, a touch of liquorice and good hoppy bitterness. Dry, bitter coffee finish. Excellent drinking condition; mostly sticky sediment.

Availability

From most major supermarkets and off-licence chains.

Tesco India Pale Ale

ABV 5%	Bottle size 500 ml	Serve at 10° C

Ingredients   Maris Otter pale malt; Fuggle and Golding hops

Fermented in the Burton Union sets, this IPA is matured, filtered and re-seeded with yeast. Priming sugars are added as required. The best before date is set at six months after bottling, although Marston's advise drinking it within three months for the best flavour. The beer was first brewed in 1994 and is a variant of the India Pale Ale which was produced for the Head Brewer's Choice scheme. Marston's own bottled IPA is stronger (5.5%) but is not bottle-conditioned.

Tasting Notes

Smooth, sweet malt is gradually overcome by dry, citric hops in the taste of this easy drinking, copper-coloured bitter. The aroma is malty, sweet and hoppy; the finish is dry, bittersweet and hoppy. Not a particularly aggressive beer and not as full and hoppy as traditional IPAs. Good condition; light sticky sediment.

Availability
From Tesco.

The Independents

Mildmay

The Mildmay Brewery, Holbeton, Plymouth, Devon PL8 1NA. Tel. (01752) 830302
Fax (01752) 830540

Mildmay began brewing in 1993, for its tied house, the Mildmay Colours Inn. In 1994, the brewery was expanded to triple its capacity to around 50 barrels per week and the beers can now be found throughout Devon and the South-West.

Patrick's Cream Stout

ABV 4.2%	Bottle size 500 ml	Serve at 13° C

Ingredients	Pipkin pale, chocolate, roasted and crystal malts; Target and Golding hops

A beer named after a director of the company – and a very fitting name, too, for a beer of this ilk. The shamrock on the label is another give away. Patrick's has been in production as a cask stout since 1993 but, like the Old Horse Whip opposite has only recently made the transformation to bottle. The cask is matured at the brewery for a couple of weeks, secondary yeast is added and then the beer is run off into bottles by a contract bottler. The long term prognosis is still unclear but the brewery confirms that Patrick's improves at least up to eight months after bottling.

Tasting Notes

A very dark ruby-red beer with a creamy coffee nose. The roast Malt taste is initially sweetish and fairly thin-bodied, becoming increasingly bitter and dry. Very dry bitter coffee finish.
Good drinking condition; light, mostly, sticky sediment.

Availability
Contact the brewery for latest stockists.

Old Horse Whip

ABV 5.7%	Bottle size 500 ml	Serve at Room Temperature

Ingredients	Pipkin lager malt; Saaz hops

With cask beers named Tipster, SP and 50/1 in its stable, it's not surprising that Mildmay also gives the Old Horse Whip a crack. This is also available in cask form (and has been since 1994), though the bottled variety is relatively new. It is described as a 'strong pale ale' but surely has much to tempt lager drinkers courtesy of its very light colouring and the pilsner tang of the Saaz hop. For the bottle (prepared once a fort-night), the cask brew is kräusened with wort from the next batch in production and then is given a dose of secondary yeast, before bottles are filled direct from the cask (off-site). Bottles should be drunk within twelve months of capping. Mildmay has high hopes for Old Horse Whip, borne out by the interest shown in the beer by the local restaurant trade and the fact that it picked up a gold medal at the 1997 International Food Exhibition.

Tasting Notes

A golden beer with a citrus fruit nose and a smooth, bittersweet taste of citrus fruit before a dry, bitter finish. It doesn't drink its strength. Excellent drinking condition; very sticky sediment.

Availability

Contact the brewery for latest stockists.

The Independents

Mole's

Mole's Brewery (Cascade Drinks Ltd.), 5 Merlin Way, Bowerhill, Melksham, Wiltshire SN12 6TJ. Tel. (01225) 704734 Fax (01225) 790770

Mole's Brewery was established in 1982 by former Ushers brewer Roger Catté (the brewery name came from his nickname).

Brew 97

ABV 5%	Bottle size 500 ml	Serve at 12–13° C

Ingredients   Maris Otter pale and crystal malts; WGV, Bramling
Cross and Fuggle hops

The 97th brew to leave the brewery (hence its name), Brew 97 was first produced in
cask form for the Bath Beer Festival in 1984. This bottled version, complete with classy
black, red and gold label, is simply filled from the cask and is made available every six
months or so. For the usual legal reasons, each bottle carries a best before date, but
the brewery modestly declares that the beer is 'always at its best'.

Tasting Notes

A mid-brown-coloured, unusual beer with a very malty, toffeeish
nose. Malt, fruit and some toffee are apparent in the taste, too, with
a good kick of bitter hops providing contrast at the end. The tangy,
bitter finish is quite warming and lingers. Good drinking condition;
very little sediment.

Availability

From Mole's pubs and some other pubs, Firkin off-licences and small off-licences. Bulk
orders shipped to overseas customers only.

The Independents

Moulin

Moulin Hotel & Brewery, Kirkmichael Road, Pitlochry, Perthshire & Kinross PH16 5EW.
Tel. (01796) 472196 Fax (01796) 474098

Moulin brewery was opened in August 1995 at the Moulin Hotel in Pitlochry, during celebrations for the hotel's 300th anniversary (the hotel housed a brewery when it first opened in 1695, so it was deemed fitting to recommence brewing on the site). The operation has since moved to the Old Coach House opposite.

Ale of Atholl

ABV 4.5%	Bottle size 500 ml	Serve at 13° C

Ingredients	Maris Otter pale, crystal, chocolate and roast malts; Fuggle hops

Now brewed weekly, Ale of Atholl (taking its name from the brewery's location in the Vale of Atholl) was first bottle-conditioned in late 1996. It's the same brew as the cask-conditioned version. The cask is allowed to settle for three days, then the beer is racked off and re-seeded with the same yeast strain. Some sugar is added and the beer is immediately bottled in glassware overprinted with the history of Moulin village. The brewers suggest enjoying a glass with venison (Scottish, of course).

Tasting Notes

A ruby-coloured beer with a slightly malty aroma, a sweetish Scots bitter taste and a lightly sweet finish (brewery's own notes – no sample supplied).

Availability

From local Thresher, The Beer Cellar (mail order), plus mail order direct from the brewery.

The Independents

Old Luxters

Old Luxters Farm Brewery, Hambleden, Henley-on-Thames, Oxfordshire RG9 6JW.
Tel. (01491) 638330 Fax (01491) 638645

Old Luxters was set up in 1990 in a 17th-century barn by David Ealand, owner of
Chiltern Valley Wines. Apart from the brewery and vineyard, the site also houses a
fine art gallery and a cellar shop.

Vintage Ale

ABV 4.5%	Bottle size 500 ml	Serve at 12° C

Ingredients	Halcyon pale, crystal and chocolate malts; Fuggle and Golding hops

If there was a prize for the best-looking bottle in this book, Vintage Ale's would come close. The bottle is actually a jug, complete with handle and a Grolsche-style swing-stopper. Red screen printing conveys the necessary information and the whole package is presented in a handcrafted wooden box. Vintage Ale is Old Luxters second bottled beer and was introduced in 1996. It's darker and more malty than the Barn Ale detailed overleaf, on account of the greater percentage of chocolate and crystal malts used. Drink it up within twelve months, as suggested by the best before mark.

Tasting Notes

An orange-brown beer with malt, fruit and hops in the aroma. The taste is mostly malty and bitter but with an unusual peachy flavour before a very dry, bitter, fruit and nuts finish. Easy drinking and full-flavoured. Lowish condition; mostly sticky yeast.

Availability

From the brewery, including by mail order. Overseas orders are taken and credit cards are accepted.

Barn Ale

ABV 5.4%	Bottle size 500 ml	Serve at 12° C

Ingredients Halcyon pale, crystal and chocolate malts;
Fuggle and Golding hops

Taking its name from the brewery's location, Barn Ale is considerably stronger than the cask ale of the same name (4.5%). It may not be as distinctively packaged as Vintage Ale but it certainly doesn't lack elegance, the bottle being tall and slim, the lettering screen-printed in gold and a tamperproof paper seal covering the cap. It was first brewed in 1993 and is deemed to improve month by month in the bottle. Even though the best before date is set one year from bottling, it may be worth persevering a little longer for even better flavour. The brewery reckons it's a good accompaniment to strong foods, such as cheese or even a curry.

Tasting Notes

A well-crafted, dark copper beer, combining fruit, malt and hops in a good body. Malty, orange fruit nose; dry, fruity, bittersweet finish. Very good condition; mostly sticky yeast.

Availability

From local Waitrose and from the brewery, including by mail order. Overseas orders are taken and credit cards are accepted.

Pilgrim

Pilgrim Ales, The Old Brewery, West Street, Reigate, Surrey RH2 9BL. Tel. (01737) 222651 Fax (01737) 225785

Set up in 1982, and moved to Reigate in 1985, Pilgrim Brewery's beers have won both local and national awards. The range of bottled beers has been expanded in recent years.

Progress

ABV 4.3%	Bottle size 500 ml	Serve at 12° C

Ingredients	Maris Otter pale, crystal and chocolate malts; Styrian Golding and East Kent Golding hops

This is a slightly stronger version of Pilgrim's cask best bitter of the same name. Like all the brewery's bottled beers, it is put into conditioning vessels after primary fermentation then shipped to Forest Bottling in Gloucestershire for bottling. The beers are not filtered and no primings are used. All the beers carry a six-month best before date.

Tasting Notes

No sample or tasting notes supplied.

Availability

From specialist off-licences and from the brewery (including by mail order).

Royal Gold

ABV 5%	Bottle size 500 ml	Serve at 10° C

Ingredients	Maris Otter pale malt; East Kent Golding and First Gold hops

Brewed to commemorate the 50th wedding anniversary of The Queen and Prince Philip, this beer has been produced in bottles with two different commemorative labels. One has a 'half torn away' style, revealing a 1940's-style label behind the 1997 version. Only 1,947 of this type are being made available.

Tasting Notes

No sample or tasting notes supplied.

Availability

From local Tesco, specialist off-licences and from the brewery (including by mail order).

Springbock

ABV 5.2%	Bottle size 500 ml	Serve at 12° C

Ingredients	Maris Otter pale malt; wheat malt; East Kent Golding hops

This is Pilgrim's wheat beer and is recommended to be served cloudy, though if you want to let it settle and drink it clear the brewery sees no problem with that!

Tasting Notes

No sample or tasting notes supplied.

Availability

From specialist off-licences and from the brewery (including by mail order).

Pudding

ABV 6.8%	Bottle size 500 ml	Serve at 12° C

Ingredients	Maris Otter pale, crystal and chocolate malts; East Kent Golding hops

This beer is only brewed every December, as you might expect.

Tasting Notes

The very sweet fruitiness of this red-brown beer is prominent right from the aroma, but the taste is not cloying and remains fairly dry. The finish is more bitter but still largely sweet, fruity and dry. Good drinking condition; fine loose sediment.

Availability

From local Asda, specialist off-licences and from the brewery (including by mail order).

The Independents

Pitfield

Pitfield Brewery, The London Beer Company Ltd., 14 Pitfield Street, Hoxton, London
N1 6EY. Tel. (0171) 739 3701

Pitfield Brewery, founded in 1981, was revived in July 1996, next to The Beer Shop
off-licence. During the previous six years, its brands had been produced at various
breweries around the country. Now the installation of new equipment means the
award-winning beers have returned home.

Pitfield Bitter

ABV 3.7%	Bottle size 500 ml	Serve at 13° C

Ingredients	Maris Otter pale and crystal malts; wheat malt; Fuggle, Challenger and East Kent Golding hops

Pitfield's standard bitter was one of their earliest brews. For bottling (like all the beers listed below), it is matured in cask for two to three weeks before being racked mostly bright. New yeast is added as required to the bottle, with maltose syrup primings to encourage a good secondary fermentation. The bottles are kept at the brewery for at least two weeks before release, although, with most supplies going only as far as next door to The Beer Shop, a close eye on conditioning can easily be maintained. Supplies move so quickly that only six months is specified as a best before date, but bottles are likely to keep much longer and the stronger beers, in particular, should improve.

Tasting Notes

An orange/gold-coloured beer with a powerful, appetisingly hoppy nose. The taste is dry and hoppy with gentle malt behind. Very dry, hoppy finish. Excellent drinking condition; mostly sticky sediment.

Availability

From The Beer Shop, including by mail order (mixed cases of twelve bottles; telephone number as for the brewery).

Shoreditch Stout

ABV 4%	Bottle size 500 ml	Serve at 13° C

Ingredients	Maris Otter pale malt; roast barley; flaked barley; Fuggle, Challenger and Target hops

Not as 'stout' as some stouts, this is a new brew from Pitfield.

Tasting Notes

No sample or tasting notes supplied.

Availability

From The Beer Shop, including by mail order (mixed cases of twelve bottles).

Amber Ale

ABV 4.2%	Bottle size 500 ml	Serve at 13° C

Ingredients	Maris Otter amber and crystal malts; wheat malt; torrefied wheat; Fuggle, Challenger and East Kent Golding hops

Amber Ale is another new beer in the Pitfield stable.

Tasting Notes

Hops and sweet malt merge in the aroma of this appropriately amber-coloured beer. Fresh, fruity, nutty malt flavours fill the mouth, with excellent hop balance, before a bitter fruit finish. Good drinking condition; mostly sticky sediment.

Availability

From The Beer Shop, including by mail order (mixed cases of twelve bottles).

Black Eagle

ABV 5%	Bottle size 500 ml	Serve at 13° C

Ingredients   Maris Otter pale, crystal and black malts;
wheat malt; Fuggle, Challenger and Styrian Golding hops

Black Eagle may ring a few bells with drinkers acquainted with Pitfield beers of old. It is reminiscent of the brewery's famous Dark Star, *Champion Beer of Britain* in 1987, although this latter beer is now owned and brewed by Dark Star Brewery, based in Brighton.

Tasting Notes

A very dark ruby-coloured beer, with an aroma of ripe red berry fruits. The taste is smooth and fruity but with some dark malt flavour and good hop balance. Fairly dry, it doesn't drink its strength and is topped by a dry, mostly bitter, lingering finish. Excellent drinking condition; fairly loose sediment.

Availability

From The Beer Shop, including by mail order (mixed cases of twelve bottles).

Honey Ale

ABV 5%	Bottle size 500 ml	Serve at 13° C

Ingredients	Maris Otter pale and crystal malts and caramalt; wheat malt; torrefied wheat; honey; East Kent Golding hops

Honey is one of the vogue ingredients in brewing, with Vaux's Waggle Dance probably the best-known honey beer. Pitfield's Honey Ale again reveals just how much fun you can have by experimenting with beer and is one of only a few bottle-conditioned examples. Sure to give you a buzz.

Tasting Notes

The first thing to be said is that honey does not dominate this amber-coloured beer. It remains delicately in the background, providing a sweet balance and softening the texture. There's a hint of it in the nose, hiding behind nutty malt and hops, and it seeps into the taste after fruit, nutty malt and hop bitterness have had their say. It is perhaps more prominent in the finish, which is bittersweet. Excellent drinking condition; heavy, mostly sticky sediment.

Availability
From The Beer Shop, including by mail order (mixed cases of twelve bottles).

Liquorice Porter

ABV 5%	Bottle size 500 ml	Serve at 13° C

Ingredients	Maris Otter pale, crystal and black malts; liquorice; East Kent Golding hops

One of two liquorice beers in this book (see also Tomlinson's), Pitfield's porter marries the traditional dark, roast, bitter flavours of this old beer style with the complementary tang of liquorice. The flavouring is added in stick form during the copper boil.

Tasting Notes

This is a fine, unusual drink in which liquorice enhances the familiar porter flavours but does not dominate. Very dark ruby-red in colour, it has an intriguing nose of roast grain, some sweetness and liquorice, before a smooth, sweetish, roasty taste with gentle bitterness and liquorice flavour. Dry, liquorice finish. Excellent drinking condition; sticky sediment.

Availability

From The Beer Shop, including by mail order (mixed cases of twelve bottles).

The Beer Shop's 15th Anniversary Ale

ABV 6%	Bottle size 500 ml	Serve at 13° C

Ingredients	Maris Otter pale, crystal, amber, black and chocolate malts; wheat malt; East Kent Golding and Cascade hops

Though the off-licence adjoining Pitfield Brewery is more than fifteen years old, it only became The Beer Shop in 1982, when the current owner, Martin Kemp, took control (it was previously known as the Two Brewers). By focusing on unusual bottled beers from around the world, the shop quickly became a magnet for beer enthusiasts. This beer commemorates its success to date.

Tasting Notes

A dark ruby-red beer with an unusual aroma – like a dry red wine's, but with some hop. The fruity, sweetish and mellow taste recalls black grapes or red berries, but there's also some dark malt flavour and good hop balance. Thinnish, fruity and mildly bitter finish. Excellent drinking condition; heavy, mostly sticky sediment.

Availability
From The Beer Shop, including by mail order (mixed cases of twelve bottles).

Millennium 2000 Ale

ABV 10.5%	Bottle size 375 ml	Serve at 13° C

Ingredients	Maris Otter pale, amber and brown malts; Challenger and East Kent Golding hops

Thankfully (considering its ABV) bottled in smaller quantities than the other Pitfield beers, this is one beer to put away for a few years, as its name implies. For this reason, no tasting notes have been included here.

Availability

From The Beer Shop, including by mail order (mixed cases of twelve bottles).

Princetown

Princetown Breweries Ltd., The Prince of Wales, Tavistock Road, Princetown, Devon
PL20 6QF. Tel. (01822) 890789 Fax (01822) 890719

Princetown Brewery was established in 1994 by a former Gibbs Mew and Hop Back
brewer.

Jail Ale

ABV 4.8%	Bottle size 500 ml	Serve at 12° C

Ingredients	Pipkin pale and crystal malts; wheat malt; Challenger and Progress hops

Based, as it is, just a short tunnelling distance from the famous prison, what else could the brewery call their premium beer? This bottled version of an award-winning cask ale is now brewed weekly and, before bottling, is racked bright and re-seeded with yeast and fresh wort. The best before date is set six months after bottling takes place but the brewery expects the beer to last well beyond this date, indeed to continue to improve for up to four years or more. Note the ominous silhouette of a judge on the yellow label.

Tasting Notes

An amber-coloured beer with an aroma of malt and citric hops. The taste is malty, sweetish and fruity but has good hop balance. Bittersweet, malty finish. Excellent drinking condition; fine sediment.

Availability

From Mildmay Brewery by mail order – tel. (01752) 830302

The Independents

Quay

The Quay Brewery, Lapin Noir Ltd., Hope Square, Weymouth, Dorset DT4 8TR.
Tel./Fax (01305) 777515

Quay was set up in summer 1996 in buildings once housing the Devenish and Groves breweries. The brewery can be visited as part of the Timewalk tourist attraction.

Groves Oatmeal Stout

ABV 4.8%	Bottle size 500 ml	Serve at 10° C

Ingredients	Pale, amber, chocolate and black malts; flaked oats; Fuggle and Bramling Cross hops

Groves is the traditional brewing name of Weymouth. Founded in 1840, it was taken over and swallowed up by Devenish in 1960. Devenish later became part of Greenalls, then Greenalls decided it didn't want to brew any more. And so the town's brewing heritage came to an undignified end. It's good to see the old name revived – and by a brewery which is housed in the old Groves buildings. This oatmeal stout comes (like the other beers overleaf) in an attractive swing-stoppered bottle which is filled on site from a conditioning tank. There is no filtration and the beer is primed only very occasionally, as and when required to boost the condition. The first batch rolled out in November 1996. A cask version is also produced.

Tasting notes

No sample or tasting notes supplied.

Availability

From the on-site off-licence.

Old Rott

ABV 5.4%	Bottle size 500 ml	Serve at 12°C

Ingredients	Pale and crystal malts; Challenger and Bramling Cross hops

Slightly more alcoholic than its cask equivalent (a 5% beer), bottled Old Rott is a strong bitter, produced about once a month. See Groves Oatmeal Stout for bottling details.

Tasting notes

No sample or tasting notes supplied.

Availability
From the on-site off-licence.

Silent Knight

ABV 5.9%	Bottle size 500 ml	Serve at 10° C

Ingredients	Pale and chocolate malts; wheat malt; Bramling Cross hops

This dark wheat beer, in the style of a German Weizenbock, may be new but it's already an award-winner. It picked up the supreme accolade at a national wheat beer championship held in London in May 1997 and looks set to capitalise on its remarkable achievement. At 5.9%, it is just a touch stronger than its cask brother of the same name and, like most wheat beers, it is designed to be drunk hazy (although, as it's so dark, it's difficult to spot the yeast anyway). See Groves Oatmeal Stout for bottling details.

Tasting notes

No sample or tasting notes supplied.

Availability
From the on-site off-licence.

Related Societies

Association Of Bottled Beer Collectors

The Association of Bottled Beer Collectors was founded in 1983 and its aims are fairly self-explanatory. Membership is £5 a year and further details can be obtained from Graham Tubb, 66 High Street, Puckeridge, Ware, Hertfordshire SG11 1RX.

The Labologists Society

Founded in 1958, and initially sponsored by Guinness, The Labologists Society is an organisation which caters, primarily, for the interests of beer label collectors. There's no doubt that a major part of the appeal of a bottled beer is in its packaging, particularly where a beautifully designed and colourful label is used. Labologists, rightly, consider these labels to be works of art and go to great lengths to unearth them. The Society holds meetings, produces an illustrated newsletter, offers advice and stages its own *Label of the Year* competition. Membership is about £12 a year and further details can be obtained from Jim Gartside, 52 Grove Avenue, London W7 3ES.

The Author's Favourites

There has been no attempt to rate or score individual beers in this book, merely to provide the facts and some guidance and to let the reader decide for him or herself which beers to seek out. To damn a beer on the basis of just a few samples also seems unfair, especially if the bottles have come from a rogue batch which has not been properly looked after somewhere along the line. However, the author has been particularly impressed with many of the beers now available and, just for the fun of it, this is his top fifteen (in no particular order).

Ballard's Old Pecker	Salopian Jigsaw
Bass Worthington White Shield	Scottish Courage Imperial Russian Stout
Freeminer Bitter	Shepherd Neame Spitfire
Fuller's 1845	Swale Old Dick
King & Barnes Old Porter	Teignworthy Beachcomber
Old Luxters Barn Ale	Woodforde's Nelson's Revenge
RCH Firebox	Wye Valley Father Christmas Ale
Ringwood Fortyniner	

The Independents

RCH

RCH Brewery, West Hewish, Weston-super-Mare, Somerset BS24 6RR. Tel. (01934) 834447 Fax (01934) 834167

This brewery was originally installed behind the Royal Clarence Hotel at Burnham-on-Sea in the early 1980s, but since 1993 brewing has taken place on a commercial basis on this site.

Pitchfork

ABV 4.3%   **Bottle size 500 ml**   Serve at 13° C

Ingredients   **Pale malt; Fuggle and Golding hops**

First brewed in 1993, this bottled beer is the same brew as the draught ale of the same name – derived from the local 1688 Pitchfork Rebellion. The best before date is set at six months post-bottling (which is carried out for the brewery – for all three of the beers – by Forest Bottling in Gloucestershire).

Tasting Notes

A golden beer with an appealing, mouth-wateringly fruity nose. Initially soft and fruity to taste, it soon gains a solid, slightly perfumed hop edge. The finish is hoppy, bitter and dry. If you like hoppy beers, this is one for you. Possibly a touch too lively on the tongue; fine sediment.

Availability
From Firkin off-licences.

Old Slug Porter

ABV 4.5%	Bottle size 500 ml	Serve at Room Temperature

Ingredients	Pale, crystal and black malts; Fuggle and Golding hops

It took a brave brewery to name a beer this, but it doesn't seem to have deterred drinkers. Like Pitchfork and Firebox, Old Slug Porter is a variant on a cask ale produced by RCH and should not be confused with a draught beer of the same name by the Hedgehog & Hogshead brew pub chain. The bottle tells you to drink it up within six months, but the brewery recommends earlier consumption (within four months) for optimum results.

Tasting Notes

A very dark red/brown porter with a deep coffee nose. Not too heavily-bodied, it nonetheless has bags of taste – good, bitter coffee with some sweetness, nuttiness and hops behind. Very full, dry finish of bitter coffee. Lively condition.

Availability

From local Tesco, Firkin off-licences and The Beer Cellar (mail order).

Firebox

ABV 6%	Bottle size 500 ml	Serve at 13° C

Ingredients   Pale and chocolate malts; Progress and Target hops

RCH's premium strength cask and bottle-conditioned beer, distinctively red in colour. Once again the best before date is posted as six months after bottling.

Tasting Notes

A very flavoursome, bronze-coloured, strong bitter with a full, hoppy and malty nose. The taste is very fruity, alive with zesty orange flavour, backed with citric hop bitterness and some dark malt. Dry, tangy, bitter orange finish, with a hint of dark malt. Good drinking condition; fine loose sediment.

Availability

From Firkin off-licences and The Beer Cellar (mail order).

Rebellion

Rebellion Beer Company, Unit J, Rose Business Estate, Marlow Bottom Road, Marlow, Buckinghamshire SL7 3ND. Tel./Fax (01628) 476594

Opened in 1993, Rebellion helps to fill the gap left in Marlow by Whitbread's closure of the Wethered brewery in 1988.

Mutiny

ABV 4.8%   **Bottle size 500 ml**   **Serve at 10 -12° C**

Ingredients   Halcyon pale and crystal malts; Target and Golding hops

A slightly stronger version of the brewery's cask Mutiny, this bottle-conditioned ale first saw light of day at Christmas 1995. It is produced from a standard Mutiny gyle, with a proportion of green beer directed to a conditioning tank where a charge of whole leaf Golding hops is introduced. The beer is then warm-conditioned to fully attenuate before being fined, filtered, primed and re-seeded with a 'special' yeast and bottled. Bottles are not released from the brewery until at least three weeks have passed. Each bottle carries a shelf-life of four months. Drink it with or without the yeast.

Tasting Notes

A dark amber-coloured beer with a hoppy, fruity nose. Nicely balanced, it is fruity, malty and hoppy and becomes increasingly bitter in the dry, nutty finish. Excellent drinking condition; sticky sediment.

Availability

From the brewery (call first to ensure stocks are available).

The Independents

Ringwood

Ringwood Brewery Ltd., Christchurch Road, Ringwood, Hampshire BH24 3AP.
Tel. (01425) 471177 Fax (01425) 480273

Ringwood was set up in 1978 and moved in 1986 to attractive 18th-century buildings, formerly part of the old Tunks brewery. A new brewhouse was commissioned at the end of 1994, and a new fermenting room completed in 1995.

Fortyniner

| ABV 4.8% | Bottle size 500 ml | Serve at 10° C |

Ingredients   Maris Otter pale, crystal and chocolate malts; Challenger, Progress and Golding hops

Fortyniner first appeared in cask form in 1978, taking its name from its 1049 original gravity. This bottled version is a new development, making its debut in December 1996 and being the only bottle-conditioned beer (but not the only bottled beer) that Ringwood produces. It's the same brew as cask Fortyniner, except that a week's cold-conditioning (4°C or less) is employed to bring down the yeast count prior to bottling. No primings are added. Bottling is carried out off-site under contract. Nine months' shelf life is indicated on the label and the beer should be kept cool, as usual, during this period, though a week in warmer surroundings before final chilling and serving should improve the condition and flavour. Look for the classy black-, yellow- and racing green-coloured label bearing the Ringwood logo of a running wild boar.

Tasting Notes

Orange gold in colour, this beer has a lovely, zesty aroma of oranges and hops. Malty orange fruit is prominent in the mouth, with some sweetness, although bitterness increases as the hops kick in. The body is good and solid, but this is an easy drinking and deceptively strong ale. Dry, bitter orange peel finish. Quite lively condition; fine loose sediment.

Availability

From Firkin off-licences and the brewery.

The Independents

Salopian

The Salopian Brewing Company Ltd., The Brewery, 67 Mytton Oak Road, Shrewsbury, Shropshire SY3 8UQ. Tel./Fax (01743) 248414

This, the first brewery in Shrewsbury for 30 years, began production in August 1995 in a former dairy in Copthorne on the outskirts of the town. The brewer is Martin Barry, formerly of the Snowdonia Brewery. Bottle-conditioned beers were introduced in February 1996 and were initially brewed on site, but these are now brewed and bottled under Martin's guidance at King & Barnes. The cask beers (including versions of all the bottled beers) are still produced at Salopian.

Proud Salopian

ABV 4%	Bottle size 500 ml	Serve at 13° C

Ingredients	Maris Otter pale, crystal and dark malts; Fuggle, Golding and Styrian Golding hops

Named after Thomas Southam, a Shropshire brewer known as 'the Proud Salopian', this beer was introduced in 1997. As with all Salopian's bottled beers, the recipe is the same as for the cask beer, and the brew is not primed or re-seeded with yeast for the bottle. For all Salopian's beers the brewery's advice is to chill for half an hour before pouring and then use a pint glass to accommodate the (often lively) head. Although all the beers are declared to be at their best after three months in the bottle, the best before date is set at one year or later.

Tasting Notes

A well-rounded, flavoursome, red-brown beer with a fresh, citric nose. Malt, hops and fruit are all evident in the mouth but the over-whelming taste is of crisp, dry bitterness. Excellent body for its strength. Clean, hoppy, bitter fruit finish. Lively condition; fairly heavy loose sediment.

Availability

From Oddbins, specialist off-licences, The Beer Cellar (mail order) and from the brewery's own shop.

Choir Porter

ABV 4.5%	Bottle size 500 ml	Serve at 13° C

Ingredients	Maris Otter pale, crystal and chocolate malts; Fuggle hops

Is this a beer to sing about? This recipe, I believe, was concocted during Martin Barry's days at Snowdonia Brewery but survives just as well over the border in England.

Tasting Notes

A fairly thin-bodied, very dark brown porter, very dry, bitter and smoky, with dry coffee bitterness in the finish. The nose is mostly of coffee but with an unusual, slightly smoky aroma. Good drinking condition; sediment not visible.

Availability

From Oddbins, specialist off-licences and the brewery shop.

Minsterley Ale

ABV 4.5%	Bottle size 500 ml	Serve at 13° C

Ingredients	Maris Otter pale and crystal malts; Fuggle, Golding and Styrian Golding hops

Named after Minsterley village (one of Shropshire's oldest and home to Mandy Evans, the brewery's owner), this premium ale was one of Salopian's first cask beers. It's been available in bottle-conditioned form since 1996 and, apparently, is good with meats and cheese. The label explains how Minsterley gained its name – from the Saxon 'Menestrelie', meaning church in a clearing in the forest.

Tasting Notes

A dark copper-coloured ale with an unusual aroma of orange fruit and peppery hops. The malty orange fruitiness continues in the full flavour, along with tangy, bitter hops. Bitter fruit and hop finish. A bit too lively in condition; fine loose sediment.

Availability

From Oddbins, local Tesco, specialist off-licences, The Beer Cellar (mail order) and the brewery shop.

Snapdragon

ABV 4.5%	Bottle size 500 ml	Serve at 13° C

Ingredients	Maris Otter pale and crystal malts; spices; Golding and Styrian Golding hops

Launched in time for the Chinese New Year 1997, Snapdragon is one of Britain's more unusual beers. Selected spices are added to the copper to produce a beer with a character suited to accompanying oriental foods, according to the brewery.

Tasting Notes

A copper-coloured beer which is an acquired taste. A very complex, perfumed, spicy nose with orange character preludes a scented mix of odd ingredients, including coriander and ginger, in the taste. Perfumed, hoppy finish with the warmth of ginger. Low condition; light sediment.

Availability

From Oddbins, specialist off-licences and the brewery shop.

Gingersnap

| ABV 4.7% | Bottle size 500 ml | Serve at 13° C |

| Ingredients | Maris Otter pale, crystal and pale chocolate malts; wheat malt; root ginger; Golding, Styrian Golding and Hersbrücker hops |

There's no mistaking the key ingredient of this brew. The ginger snaps out at you in the aroma and the initial taste but the acclaim the beer has received reveals that this is a better-balanced drink than most ginger-flavoured brews. It's actually a dark wheat beer with fresh root ginger added in during the boil. This is one Salopian beer which may be drunk cloudy, in the wheat beer tradition, although the label again advises to keep the yeast in the bottle. It goes well with chocolate and desserts, or perhaps even a strong cheese. Runner-up in *The Guardian's Bottle-Conditioned Beer of the Year* competition 1996.

Tasting Notes

An amber-coloured beer with a powerful ginger nose with some lemon in the background. The taste is earthy, hoppy and ginger spicy, with some malt but little sweetness. Ginger warmth and bitterness fill the dry finish. Extremely lively condition; little sediment.

Availability
From Oddbins, local Tesco, specialist off-licences, The Beer Cellar (mail order) and the brewery shop.

Jigsaw

ABV 4.8%	Bottle size 500 ml	Serve at 13° C

Ingredients	Maris Otter pale, crystal and coloured malts; oat malt; wheat malt; Fuggle and Styrian Golding hops

This unusual brew claims to be the missing piece in the British beer drinker's jigsaw and is described as a 'black wheat beer', its dark colouring contrasting sharply with the bright blue of the label.

Tasting Notes

An almost black-coloured, mellow stout with a cappuccino-like head and an aroma of fruit and chocolate. The taste is a smooth blend of citric fruit, chocolate and bitter coffee, with bitter chocolate dominating the aftertaste. Excellent drinking condition; sticky sediment.

Availability

From Oddbins, specialist off-licences and the brewery shop.

Ironbridge Stout

ABV 5%	Bottle size 500 ml	Serve at 13° C

Ingredients	Maris Otter pale, crystal and coloured malts; oat malt; roast barley; Fuggle and Cascade hops

Taking its name from Shropshire's famous Industrial Revolution town, Ironbridge Stout is an oatmeal stout which is aimed at female, as well as male, drinkers. To this end, the hop rate has been kept deliberately low, with smoothness given priority over bitterness. The use of perfumed Cascade hops adds a novel twist.

Tasting Notes

A very dark brown, almost black-coloured, beer with a cappuccino head and a pronounced aroma of coffee. The taste, though initially dry and bitter, has some pleasant sweet coffee behind which persists in the smooth, not too bitter, finish. Good drinking condition; fine loose sediment.

Availability

From Oddbins, specialist off-licences, The Beer Cellar (mail order) and the brewery shop.

Shepherd Neame

Shepherd Neame Ltd., 17 Court Street, Faversham, Kent ME13 7AX. Tel. (01795) 532206 Fax (01795) 538907

Kent's major independent brewery is believed to be the oldest continuous brewer in the country (since 1698), but records show that brewing commenced here as long ago as the 12th century.

Spitfire

ABV 4.7%	Bottle size 330/500 ml	Serve at 13° C

Ingredients	Halcyon pale and lager malts; East Kent Golding hops

Definitely one of 'The Few' when it first appeared in 1993, bottle-conditioned Spitfire (a variation on the Battle of Britain commemorative cask beer introduced in 1990) has been a market leader in this specialised field. It has since been joined, as this book reveals, by dozens of other bottle-conditioned brews but has held its place in the major supermarket chains, thanks to its quality and consistency. The recipe is the same as for the cask version, with the beer filtered and re-seeded with fresh yeast prior to bottling. There are no primings. Each bottle is allowed two weeks to condition at the brewery before shipping. The most common bottle size is 500 ml, but some 330s are also produced and Spitfire is the only bottle-conditioned beer which is sold in a clear glass bottle, so confident are the brewery that the beer will not suffer from being sunstruck. Their experience is that bottled beers need to be exposed to bright light for longer than Spitfire's six months' best before date in order to deteriorate in any way.

Tasting Notes

A bronze-coloured beer with a rich, grassy hop nose. The hops continue to dominate in the taste, supported by good, sweet malt. Quite dry and citric, it has a hoppy, bitter finish. Good drinking condition; the sediment sticks solidly to the bottom of the bottle.

Availability
From Shepherd Neame pubs, plus Tesco, Sainsbury, Waitrose, Morrison's, Thresher, Oddbins, Unwins and The Beer Cellar (mail order).

Kaltenberg Prinzregent Luitpold Weissbier

ABV 5%	Bottle size 330 ml	Serve at 6° C

Ingredients   Halcyon pale malt; wheat malt; Challenger hops

Kaltenberg is one of Germany's best-known breweries, although it is probably more famous for its home – in a fairytale Bavarian castle – and its aristocratic associations – it is still run by Prince Luitpold, great-grandson of Bavaria's last king – than the beers it produces. Brewed in Kent under contract, this wheat beer is produced according to the stipulations of the Reinheitsgebot, the German beer purity law which specifies that, apart from yeast, no ingredients except barley, wheat, hops and water may be used. Shep's also turn out a keg version, but this bottled variety – first produced in spring 1996 – is less frequently brewed. The brewing and bottling procedure is a touch complicated. After primary fermentation with a top-fermenting yeast, the beer is centrifuged, then kräusened with around ten per cent wort and re-seeded with a bottom-fermenting yeast. Once in bottle, it is warm-conditioned for three weeks at the brewery and stamped with a seven-month best before date. Being a traditional German-style wheat beer, it should be served cloudy, at lager temperature.

Tasting Notes

No sample or tasting notes supplied.

Availability
From Shepherd Neame pubs, Thresher, Unwins and The Beer Cellar (mail order).

The Independents

Summerskills

Summerskills Brewery, Unit 15 Pomphlett Farm Industrial Estate, Broxton Drive, Billacombe, Plymouth, Devon PL9 7BG. Tel./Fax (01752) 481283

Originally established in a vineyard in 1983, but closed after two years, Summerskills was relaunched by new owners in 1990 using plant from the old Penrhos brewery.

Best Bitter

ABV 4.3%	Bottle size 500 ml	Serve at 13° C

Ingredients	Triumph pale, crystal and black malts; Golding and Willamette hops

Both this and the Indiana's Bones highlighted opposite stray somewhat from the image of traditional Devon beer, largely due to the use of Willamette hops from the USA. They are worth seeking out for this novelty but are fine beers in their own right. Both are bottled straight from the cask (cask versions are also released) by Forest Bottling in Gloucestershire, and they are not filtered or primed. There are no hard and fast rules about drinking the yeast – the brewery is happy for you to make the decision. Best Bitter's best before date is set at five months after bottling. The bright yellow label displays the brewery logo, actually the ship's badge of *HMS Bigbury Bay*, reflecting Plymouth's maritime past.

Tasting Notes

This easy-drinking, bright bronze-coloured ale has similarities with a good wheat beer. The aroma is yeasty, citric, fruity and bready, with a hint of bubblegum, and the body is quite light and dry. Sweet fruity malt and crisp hops compete for attention in the almost cidery taste before a dry, mostly bitter finish. Very lively condition; loose sediment.

Availability

From Corkers Wine Warehouse in Plymouth (also mail order).

Indiana's Bones

ABV 5.6%	Bottle size 500 ml	Serve at 13° C

Ingredients	Triumph pale, crystal and black malts; Golding and Willamette hops

Initially marketed as a winter warmer, Indiana's Bones is now produced all year round in cask and bottle-conditioned form. The cask version performed well in CAMRA's *Champion Beer of Britain* awards a few years ago, whilst this bottled version was introduced in November 1995. Like the Best Bitter, this is a beer with a transatlantic feel (aided by the homage to the Harrison Ford movies on the label), but it also doffs its cap to local traditions in using only malts from the famous Tucker's Maltings in Newton Abbot. The result is a full-bodied beer that drinks well with a good Cheddar cheese (according to Summerskills). Store and serve as for Best Bitter, but you've a little longer to enjoy Indiana's Bones, thanks to its nine-month best before date.

Tasting Notes

A very interesting and enjoyable, dark brown beer with an intriguing aroma which is a little bit bready and features malt and some chocolate. Malt fills the mouth, with good bitterness and light chocolate in the background. The finish is malty with hop bitterness and again a hint of chocolate. Very lively but in good drinking condition beneath the froth; light, loose sediment.

Availability

From Firkin off-licences, Corkers Wine Warehouse in Plymouth (also mail order) and The Beer Cellar (mail order).

The Independents

Swale

The Swale Brewery Company, Unit 1, D2 Trading Estate, Castle Road, Eurolink, Sittingbourne, Kent ME10 3RH. Tel. (01795) 426871 Fax (01795) 410808

Swale Brewery opened in December 1995 in the village of Milton Regis but moved in spring 1997 to a new home in Sittingbourne. In addition to the two bottled beers listed below, a ginger beer has been successfully trialled and may soon be on the market.

Gold & Amber

ABV 5%	Bottle size 500 ml	Serve at 13° C

Ingredients	Maris Otter pale and amber malts; wheat malt; Cascade hops

First brewed in January 1997, Gold & Amber is a pale strong bitter with an American accent, thanks to the use of Cascade hops. Like the Old Dick mentioned overleaf, it is racked into a conditioning tank after primary fermentation and then racked again into another tank prior to bottling. Here priming sugars and fresh yeast are added. The brewery's move to new premises, and the extra storage space gained, will allow the beers longer conditioning time at the brewery (brewer John Davidson is aiming for two to three weeks in the bottle before release). The best before date is set six months down the line, but John is confident that both beers happily outlive this nominal deadline. Drink with or without the yeast, as preferred.

Tasting Notes

An unusual, amber-coloured beer with a resiny hop aroma over fruity malt. The taste is very fruity (almost peachy), but also nutty and malty, with a gentle hop balance. Moderate malty fruit finish. Excellent drinking condition; sticky sediment.

Availability

From the brewery, including by mail order, and local off-licences and pubs.

Old Dick

ABV 5.2%	Bottle size 500 ml	Serve at 13° C

Ingredients	Maris Otter pale and crystal malts; unmalted barley; Challenger hops

Swale's first foray into bottling, Old Dick (named after the brewer's father-in-law) began life in January 1996 as a cask-conditioned seasonal beer. This bottle-conditioned version was introduced in late 1996 and shortly after picked up a silver medal at the 1997 *Beauty of Hops* competition. Only slightly stronger than the Gold & Amber, but quite a different beer, it is prepared for the bottle in the same fashion and should be consumed in the same way.

Tasting Notes

This novel, dark ruby-red beer has a rich, creamy and fruity aroma, a creamy, fruity and malty taste with good bitterness, and a lingering, very bitter finish. Good drinking condition; mostly loose fine sediment.

Availability

From the brewery, including by mail order, and local off-licences and pubs.

The Independents

Tally Ho!

Tally Ho! Country Inn Brewery, 14 Market Street, Hatherleigh, Devon EX20 3JN.
Tel. (01837) 810306

The Tally Ho! recommended brewing at Easter 1990, reviving the tradition of the former New Inn brewery on the same site. New owners took over in 1994.

Hunter's Ale

ABV 5.1%	Bottle size 330 ml	Serve at 13° C

Ingredients   Pale, crystal and chocolate malts; Golding hops

First brewed in 1995, Hunter's Ale is a special brew for the bottle only – no cask version exists. This strong bitter is now brewed once a month and is racked into nine-gallon casks prior to bottling. It matures in cask for two months before being fined and re-seeded with the same strain of yeast when bottled. The best before date of plus twelve months is hand-written on the label, but the beer, according to brewery owner Megan Leonard, easily improves beyond this time. Hunter's Ale can also be custom-labelled for celebrations, etc., if you fancy placing a sizeable order.

Tasting Notes

No sample or tasting notes supplied.

Availability

From the brewery and one or two local off-licences.

Thurgia/Creber's

ABV 6%   **Bottle size 450 ml**   **Serve at 13° C**

Ingredients   Pale, crystal and black malts; Golding and Styrian Golding hops

Characterised by its Grolsche-style swing-top bottle, this beer is brewed once a month, chiefly for Creber's delicatessen in Tavistock. It can also be bought under its real name of Thurgia from the brewery. Thurgia is Greek for 'natural magic', an appropriate enough title for a bottle-conditioned brew, though the beer is also sold in cask form and made its debut in 1991. The bottling procedure mirrors that of Hunter's Ale, but each label is individually numbered, as well as dated, by hand. Like Hunter's, it should prove more than drinkable after the one-year best before limit is breached. Megan, whose background is in the wine industry, advises opening the bottle an hour before drinking, to give the brew time to settle. Pour carefully, leaving a quarter of an inch or so of yeasty residue in the bottle. Store as for Hunter's Ale.

Tasting Notes

No sample or tasting notes supplied.

Availability

From Creber's delicatessen in Tavistock, or, as Thurgia, from the brewery.

The Independents

Teignworthy

Teignworthy Brewery, The Maltings, Teign Road, Newton Abbot, Devon TQ12 4AA.
Tel. (01626) 332066

Teignworthy Brewery was founded in June 1994 with a fifteen-barrel plant by former Oakhill and Ringwood brewer John Lawton, using part of the historic Victorian malthouse of Edward Tucker & Sons. Tucker's Maltings is now an important and fascinating tourist attraction, enjoyed by thousands of Devon holidaymakers each year.

Reel Ale/Edwin Tucker's Devonshire Prize Ale

ABV 4%	Bottle size 500 ml	Serve at 13° C

Ingredients	Maris Otter pale and crystal malts; Willamette, Golding, Bramling Cross and Omega hops

Reel Ale is Teignworthy's standard cask bitter. When bottle-conditioned, it is sold as Reel Ale and also as Edwin Tucker's Devonshire Prize Ale in the Maltings Bottled Beer Shop, largely (one thinks) as an attempt to catch the eye of the many holidaymakers the Maltings attracts each year. Why bother with a dreary tub of clotted cream for Auntie May when you can send her some invigorating Devonshire real ale? Indeed, as a tourist gift, this (and the other Teignworthy beers) carry some authenticity. Unlike anonymous packets of fudge customised by sticking a postcard on the front, this is a product brewed and bottled on the premises. The recipe is the same as used for the cask beer, except that the bottled beer is filtered and re-pitched with new yeast (a different strain to that employed in primary fermentation). A twelve-month best before date is marked on each bottle and the brewery suggests that this beer is indeed best consumed before this time.

Tasting Notes

This orange gold-coloured beer is quite thin in body and is pleasant to taste without being spectacular. Its dry flavour is a mix of orange fruit, malt and hops, preceded by a gentle aroma of fruit, malt and citric hops. The finish is of bitter oranges and is moderately dry. Good drinking condition; fairly sticky sediment.

Availability

From the brewery as Reel Ale (plus mail order) and from Tucker's Maltings shop as Edwin Tucker's Devonshire Prize Ale (plus mail order, tel. (01626) 334734 – ask for Brian Gates).

Spring Tide

ABV 4.3%	Bottle size 500 ml	Serve at 13° C

Ingredients   Maris Otter pale and crystal malts; Willamette, Golding, Bramling Cross and Omega hops

Named after the high tides which wash up the Teign estuary adjacent to the brewery, this best bitter is brewed every four months or so and is also made available in cask form. The bottling procedure and advice for drinking are as for Reel Ale. The brewery recommends it as an accompaniment to cheese.

Tasting Notes

A crisp, refreshing and enjoyable, copper-coloured beer with a zesty orange nose. Fruit and malt continue into the taste which has a light, citric hop balance. Dry, bitter orange finish. Fairly lively condition; quite heavy sediment.

Availability

From local Tesco, the brewery and Tucker's Maltings shop (details as for Reel Ale).

Beachcomber

ABV 4.5%	Bottle size 500 m	Serve at 13° C

Ingredients	Maris Otter pale malt; Willamette, Golding, Bramling Cross and Omega hops

Described as a lager on the label, Beachcomber is named after the serendipitous summer hobby of local tourists and was devised as a pale beer for swigging at barbecues on summer evenings. A bottom-fermenting yeast is used but otherwise the brewing procedure is as for Teignworthy's other bottled beers and bottles are prepared every four months.

Tasting Notes

A golden beer with a rich, citric hop nose with sweet malt behind. The full taste is a very pleasant combination of sweet, light malt and excellent hoppiness, with hints of blackcurrant in the background. Bittersweet, hoppy finish. Good drinking condition; mostly sticky sediment.

Availability

From local Tesco, the brewery and Tucker's Maltings shop (details as for Reel Ale).

Maltsters Ale

ABV 5%	Bottle size 500 ml	Serve at 13° C

Ingredients	Maris Otter pale and crystal malts; Willamette, Golding, Bramling Cross and Omega hops

Not many breweries recommend that one of their beers be drunk with pickled onions, but that's what Teignworthy consider to go well with Maltsters Ale. This was a innovative brew when first prepared in 1996 as it used the new barley strain Regina, but the brewer has now switched to Maris Otter. The beer is sold on draught in winter and this bottled version is brewed twice a year, using the same bottling techniques as described for the other Teignworthy beers.

Tasting Notes

A mid-brown-coloured beer with a fruity aroma, a full-bodied, well-balanced taste of malt and hops and a slightly sweet finish (brewery's own notes - no sample supplied).

Availability

From the brewery and Tucker's Maltings shop (details as for Reel Ale).

Christmas Cracker

ABV 6%	Bottle size 500 ml	Serve at 13° C

Ingredients	Maris Otter pale and crystal malts; Willamette, Golding, Bramling Cross and Omega hops

This seasonal brew is also available in cask form over the festive period. The latest edition available before we went to press was the 1996 Christmas Cracker, also sold as 200th Brew (being just that from the brewery) and considered by its makers to be the best example yet of this strong, dark ale. The labels are freshly designed each year (Teignworthy use them as Christmas cards), the 1996 label being as red as Santa's suit, with best wishes hand scribbled by the production team on one side and a thank you message to customers printed on the other. See the description of Reel Ale for the bottling procedure.

Tasting Notes

A zesty, citric nose with some treacle and chocolate, preludes a smooth, fruity taste with a hint of chocolate and good, balancing bitterness – not too sweet but full-flavoured and warming. Bitterfruit tingles in the aftertaste, with again chocolate becoming evident. Orange brown in colour. Excellent drinking condition; fine, loose sediment.

Availability

From the brewery and Tucker's Maltings shop (details as for Reel Ale).

Edwin Tucker's Devonshire Strong Ale

ABV 8%	Bottle size 330 ml	Serve at 13° C

Ingredients	Maris Otter pale and crystal malts; Willamette, Golding, Bramling Cross and Omega hops

Like Edwin Tucker's Devonshire Prize Ale, this beer's label is enhanced by a faded old photograph of the man himself, his autograph adding authenticity. Even though it is described by the brewery as an old ale, and has the alcoholic punch of winter beer, it is brewed every six months (the first time being November 1996). It is sold only by the shop at Tucker's Maltings which, in effect, commissioned the brew. The brewery reckons it drinks like a red wine and recommend you try it with your Sunday lunch. Though the best before date is, as for the other beers, set twelve months ahead, this is one beer Teignworthy hopes will mature beyond that time because of its heavy maltiness. It is bottled in the same way as Reel Ale.

Tasting Notes

A dark ruby-red beer with a deep, fruity, malty nose, backed with some hop spice and caramel. The full, warming taste is sweetish and malty but with bitterness always present. The lingering finish is fairly dry, bittersweet and malty, with hints of sherry. Excellent drinking condition; sticky sediment.

Availability
From Tucker's Maltings shop (details as for Reel Ale).

The Independents

Three Tuns

The Three Tuns Brewing Company Ltd., Bishop's Castle, Shropshire SY9 5BW.
Tel./Fax (01588) 638797

The Three Tuns is one of Britain's great historic brew pubs, famously one of only four remaining before CAMRA began to champion real ale production. Although its brewhouse is classically Victorian, in the tower tradition, the pub first obtained a brewing licence way back in 1642. It ceased brewing in 1996 but new owners took over in the summer of that year and re-opened the brewery.

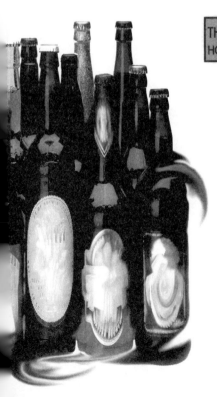

Cleric's Cure

ABV 5%	Bottle size 500 ml	Serve at 13° C

Ingredients	Maris Otter pale malt; Fuggle and Golding hops

The Three Tuns may still be a small brewery but its bottling technique for this, its only bottled beer, is as sophisticated as some of the larger concerns. After conditioning in tanks, the beer is filtered, re-seeded with yeast and then primed to ensure a good secondary fermentation in the bottle. The samples I tried were from the first trial bottling (from March 1997) and successful they were. The aim is to repeat the process at least once a month. Whilst long-term forecasts about drinkability are understandably vague, the best before date is currently set at six months, with caution clearly the watchword, but the brewery claims it will undoubtedly keep longer. The recipe is new but takes its name from a letter allegedly written to John Roberts, the former owner and brewer, in 1899. The letter is from a local vicar and urges Roberts to send more beer (he being 'the only man who has discovered a cure for agricultural depression'). The beer was to be for the enjoyment of assorted clergymen, there being 'no people in the world better judges of drink'.

Tasting Notes

A pale golden beer with an unusual malty, biscuity aroma. Sweet malt leads on the palate, with mellow, light fruit and slightly perfumed, tangy hops, before a finish of bittersweetness which has a 'fruit cocktail' flavour. A full-flavoured beer, but not too heavy – it doesn't drink its strength. Good drinking condition; light, partially loose, sediment.

Availability

From the brewery, including by mail order. Overseas orders are taken and credit cards are accepted.

The Independents

Titanic

The Titanic Brewery, Unit G, Harvey Works, Lingard Street, Burslem, Stoke-on-Trent, Staffordshire ST6 1ED. Tel. (01782) 823447 Fax (01782) 812349

This brewery, named in honour of the Titanic's Captain Smith, who hailed from Stoke, was founded in 1985 but fell into difficulties until rescued by the present owners. A move to larger premises took place in 1992 and new brewing plant was then installed in 1995. In addition to the beers listed in the following pages, Titanic has also brewed a Christmas Ale (ABV 7.2%) and has produced some bottled beers using the Victorian equipment at Shugborough Hall, home of the Staffordshire County Museum.

Titanic Stout

ABV 4.5%	Bottle size 500 ml	Serve at 13° C

Ingredients	Maris Otter pale and crystal malts; wheat malt; roast barley; Northdown, Willamette and Golding hops

Winner of *The Guardian's Best Bottle-Conditioned Beer* of 1994, Titanic Stout is also available in cask form and is simply the same beer bottled (by Burton Bridge Brewery under contract). 'Brewed in the Potteries', as the label (which is adorned with the famous ship itself) proudly declares, it can be drunk with or without the yeast. The best before date is set six months from bottling.

Tasting Notes

A beautiful, rich, dark brown/black-coloured beer with a cappuccino head and an aroma of coffee. The taste is slightly sour and extremely roasty, almost burnt, becoming bitter and finishing with a smoky, roast grain, dry and bitter aftertaste. Good body. Fine drinking condition; loose sediment.

Availability
From Firkin off-licences.

Captain Smith's Strong Ale

ABV 5.2%	Bottle size 500 ml	Serve at 13° C

Ingredients	Maris Otter pale and crystal malts; wheat malt; Yakima, Willamette and Golding hops

The unfortunate Captain Smith is depicted on the label of this powerful ale which, unlike his ill-fated vessel, has managed to reach right across the Atlantic to find US hop strains Yakima and Willamette for its recipe. For best results, drink within the six months' best before date. Like Titanic Stout, the beer is bottled by Burton Bridge and is also made available in draught form.

Tasting Notes

A distinctive ruddy brown beer with dark malt flavours on top of bitterness and fruit. Fruit and dark malt fill the aroma; bitter dark malt and fruit provide the aftertaste. Good condition; loose, silty sediment.

Availability

From Firkin off-licences.

The Independents

Tomlinson's

Tomlinson's Old Castle Brewery, Unit 5, Britannia Works, Skinner Lane, Pontefract,
W. Yorkshire WF8 1HU. Tel. (01977) 780866 Fax (01977) 690788

Marking the return of brewing to Pontefract after over 60 years, Tomlinson's was
opened in 1993. The award-winning beers recall local historical events in their names.

Three Sieges

| ABV 6% | Bottle size 330 ml | Serve at 13° C |

| Ingredients | Maris Otter pale, crystal, and pale chocolate malts; roast barley; liquorice; Challenger hops |

Rave reviews on the *Food and Drink* programme have done sales of this novel beer no harm. The distinctive ingredient is liquorice, added by the block to a traditional stout in the copper. Of course, Pontefract, with its famous cakes, has been known for its liquorice connections since the 16th century, and the 'Three Sieges' of the name also has a local link: it refers to the three sieges Oliver Cromwell laid on Pontefract Castle (depicted on the label), all of which, incidentally, came to nought. This is the same brew as the cask beer of the same name which was first produced in 1994 and, after primary fermentation, the beer is bottled on site. Brewer Sean Tomlinson suggests that you pour it from a modest height in order to whip up a good head and release some of the condition. You can drink it, the best before date declares, up to nine months/one year after bottling. Sean proposes that you experiment by adding some Three Sieges into your meat dishes, particularly venison.

Tasting Notes

An almost black beer with a tight white head. The sweet nose features roast malt and liquorice and leads into a massive, complex taste of slightly sweet, rich roast malt, before a warming, long, bittersweet liquorice finish (brewery's own notes – no sample supplied).

Availability

From local pubs and off-licences; Beer Paradise in Leeds; The Beer Cellar (mail order), plus mail order direct from the brewery.

The Independents

Tring

The Tring Brewery Company Ltd., 81–82 Akeman Street, Tring, Hertfordshire HP23 6AF. Tel. (01442) 890721 Fax (01442) 890740

Tring Brewery was established in 1992, bringing brewing back to this Hertfordshire town after over 50 years.

Death or Glory Ale

ABV 7.2%	Bottle size 275 ml	Serve at 12–14° C

Ingredients	Pale and chocolate malts; Challenger and Golding hops

You'll have to move quickly to get your hands on a bottle of this. It's only brewed once a year (annually on October 25th to commemorate the Charge of the Light Brigade in 1854 – 'Death or Glory' was the motto of the 17th/21st Lancers involved in the Charge), and most of the brew is sold as cask beer. A few gallons (in fact very few – in 1996 only nine!) are put into bottles by the brewer himself who individually numbers the labels. It's more a collector's item than a beer to consume quickly.

Tasting Notes

No sample or tasting notes supplied.

Availability

From the brewery (if you're lucky) or try these local pubs: The Kings Arms in Tring and The Greyhound in Aldbury.

The Independents

Trueman's

Sam Trueman's Brewery, The Little Brewery Co. Ltd., Henley House, School Lane, Medmenham, Buckinghamshire SL7 2HJ. Tel. (01491) 576100 Fax (01491) 571764

Henley House is a business training centre set in an idyllic spot near Marlow. Its brewery was set up in 1995 to produce real ale for delegates attending courses. The tiny plant (producing one barrel a week) has now been replaced by five-barrel equipment, in response to demand from other outlets.

Northdown Ale

ABV 4.7%	Bottle size 500 ml	Serve at 13° C

Ingredients	Pale, crystal and chocolate malts; Northdown, Fuggle and Golding hops

This is not a beer for laying down (nor is the lager), according to the brewery, who advise quick consumption and prescribe a six-month best before date. Considering the care which goes into the bottling process, you'd expect more confidence about later drinking. The beer is filtered, primed and re-seeded with yeast under a blanket of nitrogen, then bottled. It is then allowed a month to condition at room temperature. The brew is similar to the brewery's cask Best Bitter but is noticeably stronger and is brewed separately.

Tasting Notes

Fruit and chocolate dominate the aroma of this chestnut-coloured brew. The taste is dry, bitter and hoppy, with zesty fruit and hints of chocolate, before a dry, bittersweet finish with some light roast malt character and some fruit. Excellent drinking condition; heavy, loose sediment.

Availability

From the brewery, including by mail order: freephone (0800) 838689; credit cards are accepted.

True Gold Lager

ABV 6%	Bottle size 500 ml	Serve at 13° C

Ingredients   Lager malt; Saaz hops

An 'English Lager', according to the label, True Gold has taken over from an earlier bottled brew based on a cask lager called Ice Maiden. To its benefit, it is much stronger. It follows the same bottling procedure as Northdown Ale but is kept for a month at below 4° C to lager before bottling. When serving, cool the bottle but don't chill it as much as for other lagers.

Tasting Notes

A bright gold combination of sweet malt and scented hop, preceded by a hoppy, toffee malt nose and rounded off with a dry, lightly perfumed, bittersweet finish. A little cloying, but with plenty of flavour. Good drinking condition; mostly sticky light sediment.

Availability
From Waitrose and the brewery, including by mail order: freephone (0800) 838689; credit cards are accepted.

The Independents

Ventnor

Ventnor Brewery Ltd., 119 High Street, Ventnor, Isle of Wight PO38 ILY. Tel. (01983) 856161 Fax (01983) 856404

The original site of Burts Brewery is now home to Ventnor Brewery. The new ownership resurrected brewing here in summer 1996 and now supplies around 110 pubs, including one tied house.

St Boniface Golden Spring Ale

ABV 6%   **Bottle size 550 ml**   **Serve at 13° C**

Ingredients   **Pale and crystal malts; wheat malt; WGV and Omega hops**

Shortly after taking over here, the new team uncovered a hidden store of antique quart bottles at the brewery. They put these to good use in 1997 for this one-off celebration brew, commemorating the brewery's history. Only 2,000 bottles were made available, each distinctively different and packaged up in giant cylinders with plaster seals. The outside of the tough card containers featured a colourful narration of the stories of the brewery itself and of St Boniface, a Benedictine missionary born in AD 675 after whom the brewery's well is named. How many of these hand-bottled beers have actually been broached is difficult to say: having forked out around £25 for the privilege of owning one, most customers have probably put it away as a small investment or as a collectors' item. However, inspired by the interest in the beer, a more user-friendly, one-pint version is about to be released, brewed by Ventnor and bottled on the new high-tech plant at King & Barnes.

Tasting Notes

A golden beer with a hoppy nose and a malty finish. Full-bodied but also refreshing (brewery's own notes – no one-pint sample supplied).

Availability

From local off-licences, plus mail order direct from the brewery (two-pint bottles at £25 each, plus carriage).

The Independents

Viking

Viking Ales Ltd., t/a Viking Brewery, 5 Blenheim Close, Pysons Road, Broadstairs, Kent
CT10 2YF. Tel. (01843) 865211 Fax (01843) 603933

Viking Brewery was founded in 1995 and sold to the owners of the Stag & Griffin brew
pub in Buckinghamshire in 1996. The brew pub has since ceased production and its
plant has been moved here. The brewers hope you 'Take a liking to a Viking'.

Kentish Brown

ABV 5%	Bottle size 500 ml	Serve at 13° C

Ingredients	Maris Otter pale and amber malts; Fuggle hops

Bottle-conditioning is a new development at Viking and Kentish Brown may pave the way for other beers under glass (Kentish Ale is planned at 5.4 % ABV). It first appeared in October 1996 and is only available in bottled form, not in cask (the brewers believing its flavour too strong to encourage enough cask beer turnover). As its name suggests, it is a powerful brown ale and is presented in a tall, slim bottle, quite unlike the one used by that other famous Brown Ale from the banks of the Tyne. Viking's is bottled by hand from a cask and then kept at the brewery to condition for two weeks before being released to the outside world. The best before date is declared at six months, but Viking are confident (from the evidence of early samples) that this a beer which matures beyond that time.

Tasting Notes

A dark golden brown beer with a sweet, chocolaty nose. The taste is chocolaty, too, but is also dry, bitter and not over-sweet. Bitter chocolate finish. Good drinking condition; mostly sticky sediment.

Availability

From local off-licences, plus mail order direct from the brewery. Overseas orders are taken.

Bottle conditioned
Kentish Brown

The Independents

Whim

Whim Ales, Whim Farm, Hartington, Buxton, Derbyshire SK17 0AX. Tel. (01298) 84991 Fax (01298) 84702

Whim Brewery was opened in 1993 by Giles Litchfield, who is also now the owner of Broughton Brewery in Scotland.

Black Bear Stout

ABV 6.5%	Bottle size 500 ml	Serve at 13˚ C

Ingredients	Maris Otter pale and crystal malts; roast barley; Fuggle hops

Black Bear Stout was the very first beer brewed by Whim, back in 1993. It found its way into bottle for the first time a year later and is now mostly packaged up for Christmas sales. Bottling is done by Burton Bridge who take Whim casks, allow them to condition and settle and then fill the bottles without fining, filtration, re-seeding or priming. Bottles keep well for over a year, although the best before mark is somewhat less. As well as a direct cask equivalent, a slightly stronger, second cask version (7%) is produced at Christmas and is sold as Black Christmas.

Tasting notes

No sample or tasting notes supplied.

Availability

From the brewery, its one tied house, The Wilkes Head in Leek, and from Billy Bunter's off-licence in Leek.

The Independents

Wood

The Wood Brewery Ltd., Wistanstow, Craven Arms, Shropshire SY7 8DG.
Tel. (01588) 672523 Fax (01588) 673939

This village brewery was founded by the Wood family in 1980, in buildings adjacent to the Plough Inn. The brewery has enjoyed steady growth in recent years.

Shropshire Lad Spring Bitter

ABV 5%	Bottle size 500 ml	Serve at 13° C

Ingredients	Pale, crystal and chocolate malts; torrefied wheat; Fuggle and Golding hops

Wood introduced this beer in 1996, to commemorate the one hundredth anniversary of the publication of A E Housman's poem *A Shropshire Lad*. The ale is also available in cask form but is a subtly different brew (4.5% as opposed to the bottled 5%). Primary fermentation is halted slightly earlier than for the cask brew, the beer is fined and then, three or four days later, the beer is bottled (by Forest Bottling of Gloucestershire). Each bottle is considered ready to drink after a short storage period at the brewery but nine months are allowed in the shelf life date. You can drink it with or without the yeast. The apple green, rustic bottle labels (which quote Housman's statement of the obvious: 'Ale man, ale's the stuff to drink') are subtitled 'Spring Bitter', though the beer is available all year round. Wood are now considering adding further 'Shropshire Lads' for other seasons of the year.

Tasting Notes

A reddish brown beer with an initially sweetish, yet crisp and fruity character and good hop bitterness. The aroma combines hops, dark malt and a hint of lemon, whilst the bitter fruit finish is dry and hoppy. Good drinking condition; little loose sediment.

Availability

From local Tesco, Firkin off-licences and smaller supermarkets and off-licences.

Christmas Cracker

ABV 6%	Bottle size 500 ml	Serve at 13° C

Ingredients Pale, crystal and chocolate malts; Fuggle and Golding hops

Though Wood's Christmas Cracker has been warming the hearts of local drinkers for some years, this bottled version is a relative newcomer, first clinking its way off the bottling line at Christmas 1996. It's the same beer as cask, brewed several times in November, fined as draught beer after a short maturation period at the brewery and bottled (by Forest Bottling) without primings. With its full, malty body and high ABV, it can be enjoyed either cool or at room temperature and is ready to drink once released by the brewery. Like Shropshire Lad, the best before date is set at nine months later. Not surprisingly Wood consider it to be the perfect accompaniment to the rich foods of Christmas. Look out for the (very few) swing-stoppered bottles of the 1996 batch, as these have become collector's items.

Tasting Notes

A dark, rich, red-coloured beer, full-bodied, vinous and fruity, with strong roasted malt notes. Long-lasting, port-like finish (brewery's own notes – no sample supplied).

Availability

From local Tesco and smaller supermarkets and off-licences.

Woodforde's

Woodforde's Norfolk Ales (Woodforde's Ltd.), Broadland Brewery, Woodbastwick, Norwich, Norfolk NR13 6SW. Tel. (01603) 720353 Fax (01603) 721806

Founded in late 1980 in Norwich, to bring much-needed choice to a long Watney-dominated region, Woodforde's moved to a converted farm complex, with greatly increased production capacity, in the picturesque Broadland village of Woodbastwick in 1989. It brews an extensive range of award-winning beers.

Wherry Best Bitter

ABV 3.8%	Bottle size 330 ml	Serve at Room Temperature

Ingredients	Maris Otter pale and crystal malts; Fuggle and Golding hops

This bottle-conditioned version of CAMRA's *Champion Beer of Britain* 1996 is sure to be in great demand. It finds its way into the bottle (like most of Woodforde's beers) by a rather convoluted system whereby Woodforde's sell casks of beer to WNA Promotions who purchase the bottles, fill them and sell them only in Woodforde's visitor's centre shop (although mail order is now being considered). The bottles are simply filled from the cask which has been allowed a short maturation period and then primed with sugar, otherwise the beer is the same as Woodforde's sell on draught. Wherry and all the following beers should easily last at least six months, although WNA recommend that Wherry is drunk up within two for best results.

Tasting Notes

An orange gold-coloured beer with a wonderful, fruity and hoppy nose. Malt, orange fruit and bitter hops fill the mouth before a dry, bitter fruit finish. Excellent drinking condition; fine sediment. Cruelly small bottles.

Availability

From the brewery visitor's centre.

Great Eastern Ale

ABV 4.3%	Bottle size 330 ml	Serve at Room Temperature

Ingredients	Maris Otter pale malt; Fuggle and Golding hops

'A special brew to commemorate 150 years of the Great Eastern Railway in Norfolk', declares the label, confirming that Great Eastern was first brewed in 1994 as a souvenir beer. This bottled version is the same as the original draught beer, with a slight difference due to the bottling procedure, as explained in the entry for Wherry Best Bitter earlier. Like Wherry, drink within two months for maximum enjoyment.

Tasting Notes

A pleasant, well-rounded but undemanding beer, pale gold in colour. The aroma is fruity and the taste mellow and lightly fruity, with a gentle hop spice balance. Bitterness and hoppiness come through more in the finish. Good drinking condition; fine loose sediment.

Availability

From the brewery visitor's centre.

Nelson's Revenge

ABV 4.5%	Bottle size 330 ml	Serve at Room temperature

Ingredients	Maris Otter pale and crystal malts; Golding hops

Reflecting Nelson's associations with Norfolk, Nelson's Revenge is yet another of Woodforde's premium ales (they brew at least ten cask beers). Drink within six months in line with the best before date.

Tasting Notes

With an aroma of grassy hop over citric fruit, this orange gold ale has bags of character right from the first sniff. An excellent balance of fruit and malt, with some zesty, bitter hops, is a treat on the palate, with a dry, moreish bittersweet finish to round off. Very good drinking condition; watch for the fine sediment.

Availability

From the brewery visitor's centre.

Norfolk Nog

ABV 4.6%	Bottle size 330 ml	Serve at Room temperature

Ingredients	Maris Otter pale, crystal and chocolate malts; Fuggle and Golding hops

Pre-dating the success of the brewery's Wherry Best Bitter by four years, Norfolk Nog was CAMRA's *Champion Beer of Britain* 1992. To earn the supreme CAMRA accolade with two different ales is a remarkable achievement, especially for a small brewery. (For the record, only one other brewery, Fuller's, has claimed the top prize with more than one beer.) The only caveat when citing this achievement is that drinkers should be gently reminded that cask beer and bottled beer are not quite the same thing, even if the beer leaves the same cask, as in this case. The use of priming sugars and the level of carbonation can make a difference to the nature of the beer, as can the maturing process in the bottle. Follow the best before recommendation and drink within six months.

Tasting Notes

This is a very dark brown, strong mild, without the bitterness of a stout or the cloyingness of a heavy old ale. Its aroma is smooth and deeply chocolatey, characteristics which continue in the taste, which is balanced by bittering hop. The finish is one of bitter chocolate. Good drinking condition; fine loose sediment.

Availability

From the brewery visitor's centre.

Baldric

| ABV 5.6% | Bottle size 330 ml | Serve at Room temperature |

Ingredients Maris Otter pale malt and caramalt; Golding hops

First brewed in 1991 and named after the Blackadder character, Baldric is one of Woodforde's beers which it may pay dividends to put away for a while. The best before date is six months post-bottling but the strength and solid maltiness may help it survive and mature well beyond this time. From the caricature on the label you can tell this is a semi-serious brew, but does the bold self-description as 'a strong evil brew with the pungent essence of old socks' incline you to sip and enjoy? I think not.

Tasting Notes

This is a much better beer than the label suggests. Its orange gold colour hints at the orange fruitiness which dominates the aroma, with some hop spice behind. The taste is full and malty, but not overly sweet, thanks to the good bitter hop balance. The dry, lasting, gently warming finish combines fruit, malt and citric hops. Plenty of condition.

Availability

From the brewery visitor's centre.

Headcracker

ABV 7%	Bottle size 330 ml	Serve at Room Temperature

Ingredients	Maris Otter pale malt and caramalt; Golding hops

Clearly in the first division of the appropriate names league, Headcracker is not a beer to treat lightly. Its origins are in the barley wine school. In fact you could say it is now one of the class leaders, having won CAMRA's *Best Barley Wine* award on two occasions (in cask form). Like its strong stablemate Baldric, this is one to experiment with over a longer period than the prescribed six months' shelf life.

Tasting Notes

This complex barley wine has an orange gold colour and a slightly woody, fruity (oranges and peaches) nose. The powerful taste features mellow fruit (peaches again), some liquorice and good hop bitterness, but is also a little woody. Bitter fruit and a hint of liquorice tingle away in the dry aftertaste. Good drinking condition; fine loose sediment.

Availability
From the brewery visitor's centre.

Norfolk Nips

ABV 8.5%	Bottle size 180 ml	Serve at Room Temperature

Ingredients	Maris Otter pale and chocolate malts; Golding hops

Now only brewed once a year, this beer closely follows a recipe from the defunct Steward & Patteson brewery and was initially produced in March 1992 to commemorate the tenth anniversary of the local CAMRA news journal, *Norfolk Nips*. Unlike the beers listed earlier, this is not bottled by WNA Promotions and is more exclusively 'Woodforde's'. Although twelve months are suggested as the best before time, the strength and high hop rate should enable this beer to mature well beyond a year after bottling. Indeed, it has already enjoyed several months of maturation at the brewery prior to bottling.

Tasting Notes

A well-hopped yet mellow barley wine (brewery's own notes – no sample supplied).

Availability

From the brewery visitor's centre.

Wye Valley

Wye Valley Brewery, 69 St Owen Street, Hereford HR1 2JQ. Tel. (01432) 342546 Fax (01432) 266553

Wye Valley Brewery began production in 1985 and moved to these premises a year later. The brewery has since been expanded to cater for increased demand.

Brew 69

ABV 5.6%	Bottle size 500 ml	Serve at Room Temperature

Ingredients	Maris Otter pale and crystal malts; wheat malt; Target hops

First brewed in cask form in 1986, Brew 69 has only recently been produced in bottled format. It takes its name from the address of the brewery and is the same recipe as the draught version. Wye Valley see it very much as a strong English ale, a beer made with English Target hops and a drink to savour with roast meats and other English cooking. After primary fermentation, the beer is matured at the brewery then shipped to Forest Bottling in Gloucestershire where, unfiltered, it is bottled without priming sugars. For best results, drinking within three or four months is advised, although the best before date is set twelve months on from bottling.

Tasting Notes

A dark golden beer with a predominantly hoppy nose. The palate is soft, malty, fruity and sweet, with hop bitterness mounting a late charge and going on to dominate the dry finish. Excellent drinking condition; very fine loose sediment.

Availability

From Wye Valley pubs and some free trade outlets.

Dorothy Goodbody's Father Christmas Ale

ABV 8%	Bottle size 330 ml	Serve at Room Temperature

Ingredients	Maris Otter pale and crystal malts; wheat malt; roast barley; dark brown molasses; Target hops

Wye Valley seasonal cask beers all roll out under the 'Dorothy Goodbody' title. There is not, and never has been, a real Dorothy: she is just a figment of the brewery's fertile imagination, a 1950s blonde bombshell dreamt up to market the seasonal range. Beers under her name range from a Springtime Bitter to a Wintertime Ale and include a draught version of this bottled brew, which first appeared in 1995. Understandably, it is only produced once a year and, like Brew 69, is matured at the brewery before being bottled (this time by Burton Bridge Brewery). Again three–four months after bottling is the optimum drinking up time but the brewery reckon this potent ale will last much longer. The nicely balanced label, showing Dorothy in her Santa's hat, picked up an award (*Best Commemorative Label*) from the Labologists Society in 1996. One to drink with your Christmas pud.

Tasting Notes

Resiny hop and chocolate feature in the aroma of this dark ruby-red beer which has a smooth, rich, malty taste with good balancing bitterness. Pronounced liquorice finish. Excellent drinking condition; slight loose sediment.

Availability

From Wye Valley pubs and some free trade outlets.

The Nationals

Bass

Bass Brewers Ltd., 137 High Street, Burton upon Trent, Staffordshire DE14 1JZ
Tel. (01283) 511000 Fax (01283) 513435

Founded in 1777, Bass is Britain's second largest brewer, with some 23 per cent of all beer production. It produces the country's biggest selling beer brand, Carling Black Label lager, and two of its ale brands (Stones Bitter and Worthington Bitter) feature amongst the top five sellers. Draught Bass, promoted as its flagship brand, is still the biggest-selling premium cask ale. Its major bottle-conditioned beer is Worthington White Shield, although some exciting additions have been supplied by the tiny brewery at the Bass Museum in Burton upon Trent.

The Nationals

Bass Birmingham

Cape Hill Brewery, PO Box 27, Smethwick, Birmingham, W. Midlands B16 0PQ.
Tel. (0121) 558 1481

This is one of the largest cask beer breweries in the country, enjoying massive investment in recent years.

Worthington White Shield

ABV 5.6%	Bottle size 275 ml	Serve at 12°C

Ingredients	Pipkin and Halcyon pale malt; Eroica and Northern Brewer hops

For years Worthington White Shield, along with Guinness Extra Stout, was the welcome standby for serious drinkers who found themselves tragically marooned in a keg-only pub. In many ways, it's the archetypal Burton pale ale – except that it's now brewed in Birmingham, having arrived here after a short stopover in Sheffield. Great efforts have been made in recent years to pep up the image of White Shield, including the switch to non-returnable bottles, a new bottle shape and painstakingly spelled-out instructions for how to pour, much of which has been lost on supermarket clients who haven't appreciated the finer art of yeast retention. Interestingly, the recipe itself appears to have changed, too. Previously, White Shield was quoted as incorporating Challenger and Northdown hops. The latest ingredients list shows the US names Eroica and Northern Brewer. At the brewery, following primary fermentation, the beer is filtered and re-seeded with new yeast (a different strain to that used earlier in the brewing process). Primings are added if the fermentable residue in the beer is too low. Once in your possession, bottles should, according to Bass, improve with keeping up to the best before date of twelve months after filling. White Shield enthusiasts would consider that equivalent to drinking green beer: some happily tuck crates away for a rainy day long into the future. More on White Shield, its history and its significance in the story of bottle-conditioned beers can be found in *The Classics* feature at the front of this book.

Tasting Notes

A bronze-coloured, very tasty beer, preceded by a distinctive, sweetish, malty, fruity nose which also has noticeable spicy hop. Mouth-filling, rich, ripe malt, fruit, nuts and tangy, bitter hops compete for attention in the taste, with some liquorice character behind. Tangy, bitter, lingering finish. Excellent drinking condition; fairly loose but slight sediment.

Availability

From Sainsbury, local Tesco, The Beer Cellar (mail order) and specialist off-licences.

Bass Museum

Museum Brewing Company, The Bass Museum, PO Box 220, Horninglow Street, Burton upon Trent, Staffordshire DE14 1YQ. Tel. (01283) 511000 Fax (01283) 513509

This is the microbrewery within Bass's popular museum. Constructed from old plant from M&B's Cape Hill site, dating in parts from 1850 and from 1920, it was moved here in 1976 as a static display and was used initially only a couple of times a year (by other Bass brewers who liked to lark about). It became fully operational again in 1995, the first brew going in on 23 December. Housed in a former engine room, it sits in a corner of what used to be the Bass tradesmen's yard, amidst former cobblers', coppersmiths' and tailors' units.

Masterpiece IPA

ABV 5.4 %	Bottle size 500 ml	Serve at 13° C

Ingredients	Halcyon pale and crystal malts; Fuggle and Golding hops

This, the standard bottled beer, is produced and labelled to order. Whoever commissions the beer can have their own label attached and those that have taken up the offer have been the Parliamentary Beer Club, the digger firm JCB and Greenalls. According to brewer Steve Wellington, it is 'very reminiscent of Red Triangle', the Bass bottled pale ale which disappeared some time ago. After eight or nine days of primary fermentation, the beer is cooled to 10° C and kept for two weeks in closed tanks. It is then taken down to 4° C and stays in the tank until bottling (preferably two weeks, but sometimes up to three or four weeks). The night before bottling it is pumped into a holding tank where it is primed with sucrose (if the fermentability level is not adequate for the required strength or carbonation) and roused. No new yeast is added, nor is the beer deliberately filtered or fined. Bottles are then filled by hand, using an elementary six-head filler. The same bottle is used for all the museum's beers. It is a surplus Bass bottle left over after a new Scottish beer, Black Dove, had died a death. Bass had 250,000 bottles spare but they're now being put to good use, even if they appear a bit too voluminous for the stronger beers. The beers are stamped with a 'best between' date (giving an ideal drinking window), the upper limit being six months post-bottling, although they remain perfectly drinkable and possibly improve beyond this period. All can be drunk with or without the yeast, as preferred.

Tasting Notes

A bronze-coloured beer with gentle hops presiding over the malt in the aroma. The taste is initially sweet and fruity, giving way to mellow malt and tangy hop and becoming dry. The dryness continues in the finish, which is pleasantly malty, sweetish and hoppy. Good drinking condition; loose sediment.

Availability

From the museum shop. The museum itself is open 10-5 (last entries 4); the shop is open 10-6, all week.

P2

ABV 8%	Bottle size 500 ml	Serve at 13° C

Ingredients	Halcyon pale and chocolate malt; Fuggle and Golding hops.

P2 is a dark, very strong, Russian-style stout, of the sort once shipped to the imperial court of Russia during the 19th century. Culled from the Bass archives, like the other beers, the recipe is prepared for the bottle in the same way as Masterpiece IPA.

Tasting Notes

A very dark brown, almost black, beer with a honey-coloured head and a powerful aroma which combines fruit with the scent of polished leather. In the mouth, the beer is not as aggressive as expected, but instead very smooth and sweetish with good roast malt flavour and fruit in the background. The dry finish features mellow, sweetish roast malt with pleasant hop bitterness to balance. Excellent drinking condition; heavy loose sediment.

Availability
From the museum shop.

No. 1 Barley Wine

ABV 10.5%	Bottle size 500 ml	Serve at 13° C

Ingredients   Halycon pale malt; Fuggle and Golding hops

A bottle to share. No. 1 is a recreation of the famous Bass barley wine of the same name which ceased to be a few years ago. In its latter days, that beer was pasteurised but it had been enjoyed by many drinkers in its natural, bottle-conditioned form for decades. No. 1 is an intriguing beer. Its hue is dark red yet the colour is only derived from pale malt which caramelises during the extra long, twelve-hour boil which evaporates the wort down from an initial five barrels to three, beginning at 1105 OG and finishing at 1018. With three separate hop charges at various stages, however, this is no sweet, cloying mixture. The label boasts that the beer is matured in cask for over a year before it is bottled (using the same procedure employed for the other beers).

Tasting Notes

Very dark ruby in colour, this well-rounded beer has a powerful, sherry-like nose. The taste is mouth-filling, warming and exceptionally fruity with some liquorice character and good bitterness. Ultra long, creamy bitter fruit finish. Lowish condition; heavy sediment.

Availability
From the museum shop.

The Nationals

Scottish Courage

Scottish & Newcastle PLC, 111 Holyrood Road, Edinburgh, Lothian EH8 8YS.
Tel. (0131) 556 2591 Fax (0131) 558 1165

Scottish & Newcastle was formed in 1960, as a merger between Scottish Brewers Ltd. (the former Younger and McEwan breweries) and Newcastle Breweries Ltd. In 1995, S&N purchased Courage from its Australian owner, Foster's, making it Britain's largest brewing company. Scottish Courage's one remaining bottle-conditioned beer is the classic Imperial Russian Stout, a Courage (previously Barclay Perkins) product now handled at the John Smith's brewery in Tadcaster.

The Nationals

John Smith's

John Smith's Tadcaster Brewery, Tadcaster, N. Yorkshire LS24 9SA. Tel. (01937) 832091 Fax (01937) 833766

This business was founded at the Old Brewery (now home to Samuel Smith) in 1758 and was taken over by John Smith (Sam's brother) in 1847. The present brewery was built in 1884 and became part of the Courage empire in 1970.

Courage Imperial Russian Stout

ABV 10%	Bottle size 170 ml	Serve at Room Temperature

Ingredients	Pale, black and amber malts; Target hops

Imperial Russian Stout is one of the true classics of British brewing. A remnant of the 19th-century export trade to the Baltic, it is now seldom produced. The last batch was brewed at John Smith's back in 1993 and stocks of this remain (and, no doubt, continue to improve), but there is no news of where and when the next brew will go in. At the brewery, the stout is matured for a week at 20° C before two months of cold-conditioning (-1° C). The beer is then simply put into bottles (outside the brewery, under contract) without primings or extra yeast. This is not a beer to swig, but one to sip like a liqueur, perhaps with a good, strong-flavoured cheese. You should try to keep the yeast in the bottle, but this is not easy as the beer is so dark it prevents sediment detection. What is also not easy is finding bottles on sale. You may stumble across the odd pub which keeps a few dusty bottles in reserve but may have more luck overseas, as Imperial Stout is well-received in countries like Belgium, France and Switzerland. See *The Classics* feature at the front of the book for more on this potent brew.

Tasting Notes

Stout drinkers beware! This is not what you might expect. In fact, this beer is in a class of its own. Its very dark red, almost black, colouring hints at the complexity to follow in the aroma and taste. The nose has a wonderful, sherry-like character but also liquorice, strong coffee, raisins and even leather. In the mouth, the beer is warming and gum-tingling, with a slight sharpness, hop bitterness and the taste of red berry fruits. The long-lasting, very pleasant finish smacks of coffee. Lowish condition; loose sediment.

Availability

Contact Scottish Courage for latest details at Fountain House, 160 Dundee Street, Edinburgh EH11 1DQ. Tel. (0131) 656 5000

The Nationals

Whitbread

The Whitbread Beer Company, Whitbread PLC, Porter Tun House, Capability Green, Luton, Bedfordshire LU1 3LS. Tel. (01582) 391166 Fax (01582) 397397

Whitbread is the smallest of Britain's national brewers but has shown the most commitment of all the big companies to real ale in recent years. However, its only bottle-conditioned beer is produced by one of its brew pubs.

Frog & Parrot

Frog & Parrot, 64 Division Street, Sheffield, S. Yorkshire S1 4SG. Tel. (0114) 272 1280

This brew pub began production in 1982. It uses malt extract rather than whole malt to make its beers.

Roger & Out

ABV 12.5%	Bottle size 330 ml	Serve at Room Temperature

Ingredients	Malt extract; Challenger, Styrian Golding and Golding hops

This beer once had the privilege of being described in the *Guinness Book of Records* as Britain's strongest ale. That honour has since been claimed by other ridiculously strong brews but Roger & Out will always be known as the original mind-blower. It was first produced in cask form in 1982 and this bottled version followed soon after. It took its name, like other Frog & Parrot beers, from the brew pub's former manager, Roger Nowill. Today it is brewed about once a month. The cask beer is allowed two months to condition, fined and then the bottles are simply hand-filled from the cask. A rather timid six-week best before date is placed on the labels but the pub is in no doubt about the beer's longevity, even to the point where bottles are set aside for consumption over a year later. A special certificate, proclaiming the beer's reputation for potency, is awarded with each bottle purchased. If you buy three nips of the cask version, and then pick up a bottle to take home, you can also have a T-shirt!

Tasting Notes

No sample or tasting notes supplied.

Availability

From the brew pub.

Foreign Bottles

There are numerous bottle-conditioned beers brewed in other countries which are easily obtained in the UK, either through supermarkets and off-licences or through the more specialised channels of beer shops and mail order companies. The most common countries of origin are Germany, Belgium and Holland.

The key to spotting a bottle-conditioned beer from another country is, naturally enough, finding the words which mean 'with yeast' or 'bottle-fermented'. In German, look for 'mit Hefe', 'Flaschengärung' or 'naturtrüb', (naturally cloudy), but avoid 'hefe-frei' and 'ohne Hefe' as these mean yeast-free. You may also come across a beer described as 'Hefeweissbier' or 'Hefeweizenbier'. This is a wheat beer containing yeast. For Belgian beers you need the benefit of two languages. Variously, in Flemish and French, the words to find are 'op gist ', 'sur levure' or 'sur lie' (all meaning with yeast sediment), or 'hergist in de fles', 'nagisting in de fles', 'refermentée en bouteille' or 'fermentation en bouteille' (bottle-fermented). Dutch and Flemish are very similar, so on beer labels from Holland seek out the words 'op gist' or 'met gist'. Annoyingly, many beers do not state that they are bottle-conditioned but an informed shopkeeper should be able to advise. Failing that you may have to fall back on raising the bottle to the light to see if there's any sediment!

The most easily found brands from Germany are Weissbiers (wheat beers). Brewers Schneider, Erdinger, Spaten-Franziskaner, Thurn und Taxis and Löwenbräu are all well represented in the UK and supermarkets like Tesco, Sainsbury and Waitrose have their own label wheat beers which are brewed in Germany. Belgium is just as well represented, with many of its wonderful bottled beers now commonplace in our supermarkets and off-licences. These include the three Red-, White- and Blue-capped beers from the Chimay Trappist brewery, the powerful Duval from Moortgat and orange-coloured Orval, another Trappist ale. Westmalle Trappist beers may also be found but probably the most accessible Belgian bottle-conditioned beer these days is Hoegaarden White, the quenching coriander- and curaçao-flavoured beer which Whitbread distributes. From Holland you are most likely to discover one of the beers from the La Trappe monastic brewery. These three countries apart, one country stands out for its bottle-conditioned beer and this, surprisingly, is Australia, thanks to its Coopers Sparkling Ale. Coopers also produced a beer for Marks & Spencer for a while in 1996.

Index by Beers

Index By Brewery

INSTRUCTIONS TO YOUR BANK TO PAY DIRECT DEBITS

Please complete parts 1 to 4 to instruct your bank to make payments directly from your account.
Return the form to Campaign for Real Ale, 230 Hatfield Road, St Albans, Herts AL1 4LW.

To the Manager

1 Please write the full postal address of your bank branch in the space above.
2 Name(s) of account holder(s):
Address:

Post Code:

3 Account Number: ☐☐☐☐☐☐☐☐

Banks may refuse to accept instructions to pay direct debits from some types of account.
Direct debit instructions should only be addressed to banks in the United Kingdom.

☐☐☐☐☐☐ CAMRA Computer Membership No. (for office use only)

| 9 | 2 | 6 | 1 | 2 | 9 | Originator's Identification No.

4 Your instructions to the bank, and signature.

• I instruct you to pay direct debits from my account at the request of Campaign for Real Ale Limited.

• The amounts are variable and are to be debited annually.

• I understand that Campaign for Real Ale Limited may change the amount only after giving me prior notice.

• PLEASE CANCEL ALL PREVIOUS STANDING ORDER INSTRUCTIONS IN FAVOUR OF CAMPAIGN FOR REAL ALE LIMITED.

• I will inform the bank in writing if I wish to cancel this instruction.

• I understand that if any direct debit is paid which breaks the terms of this instruction, the bank will make a refund.

Signature(s)   Date

JOIN CAMRA

If you like good beer and good pubs you could be helping the fight to preserve, protect and promote them. CAMRA was set up in the early seventies to fight against the mass destruction of a part of Britain's heritage.

The giant brewers are still pushing through takeovers, mergers and closures of their smaller regional rivals. They are still trying to impose national brands of beer and lager on their customers whether they like it or not, and they are still closing down town and village pubs or converting them into grotesque 'theme' pubs.

CAMRA wants to see genuine free competition in the brewing industry, fair prices, and, above all, a top quality product brewed by local breweries in accordance with local tastes, and served in pubs that maintain the best features of a tradition that goes back centuries.

As a CAMRA member you will be able to enjoy generous discounts on CAMRA products and receive the highly rated monthly newspaper What's Brewing. You will be given the CAMRA members' handbook and be able to join in local social events and brewery trips.

To join, complete the form below and, if you wish, arrange for direct debit payments by filling in the form overleaf and returning it to CAMRA. To pay by credit card, contact the membership secretary on (01727) 867201.

Full membership £14; Joint (two people at the same address) membership £17; Life membership £168/£204. Student, pensioner, unemployed, disabled £8. Joint pensioners £11.

Please delete as appropriate:

I/We wish to become members of CAMRA.

I/We agree to abide by the memorandum and articles of association of the company.

I/We enclose a cheque/p.o. for £   (payable to CAMRA Ltd.)

Name(s)
Address

Signature(s)

CAMRA Ltd., 230 Hatfield Road, St Albans, Herts AL1 4LW

Other Books from CAMRA

The CAMRA Books range of guides helps you search out the best in beer (and cider) and brew it at home too!

Buying in the UK

All our books are available through bookshops in the UK. If you can't find a book send for a free catalogue to the CAMRA address below. CAMRA members should refer to their regular monthly newspaper *What's Brewing* for the latest details and member special offers. CAMRA books are also available by mail order (postage free) from: CAMRA Books, 230 Hatfield Road, St Albans, Herts, AL1 4LW. Cheques made payable to CAMRA Ltd. Telephone your credit card order on (01727) 867201.

Buying outside the UK

CAMRA books are also sold in many book and beer outlets in the USA and other English-speaking countries. If you have trouble locating a particular book, use the details below to order by mail or fax (+44 1727) 867670.

Carriage of £3.00 per book (Europe) and £6.00 per book (US, Australia, New Zealand and other overseas) is charged.

UK Booksellers

Call CAMRA Books for distribution details and book list. CAMRA Books are listed on all major CD-ROM book lists and on our Internet site: http://www.camra.org.uk

Overseas Booksellers

Call or fax CAMRA Books for details of local distributors.

Distributors are required for some English language territories. Rights enquiries (for non-English language editions) should be addressed to the managing editor.

Brewery Breaks

by Ted Bruning   64 pages   Price: £3.99

ISBN 1-85249-132-9

The complete guide to days out in Britain's working breweries and brewery museums. Locations, opening times and recommendations.

Kegbuster Remembers

by Bill Tidy   72 pp inc colour   Price: £4.99

ISBN 1-85249-134-5

A cartoon retrospective on the great beer issues. Laugh all the way to the bar!

CAMRA Guide to Cellarmanship

by Ivor Clissold   144 pages   Price: £6.99

ISBN 1-85249-126-4

Everything you need to know about how to keep over 300 brands of real ale. From taking delivery to pouring a pint. Fully illustrated.

CAMRA Beer and Pubs Quiz Book

by Jeff Evans   128 pages   Price: £3.99

ISBN 1-85249-127-2

Test yourself or your friends or set quizzes for pub competitions. Beer-related puzzles, crosswords and mental teasers.

Good Beer Guide to Prague & Czech Republic

by Graham Lees   256 pages   Price: £8.99

ISBN 1-85249-122-1

A comprehensive tour around the many breweries and beer outlets with tasting notes, maps, tourist information and language guide to make your stay complete. Covers pubs, beers, accommodation and food.

Good Beer Guide UK

edited by Jeff Evans – annual publication   560 pages

Price: £10.99

Let CAMRA's *Good Beer Guide* lead the way to around 5,000 great pubs serving excellent ale – all researched and revised annually by CAMRA.

Known Gems & Hidden Treasures – A Pocket Guide to the Pubs of London

by Peter Haydon   224 pages   Price: £7.99

ISBN 1-85249-118-3

If you visit London, then you need this guide to the well-known and historic pubs you must not miss, and also to the pubs which are hidden gems. Discover pubs with theatrical, sporting and historical connections.

Room at the Inn

by Jill Adam   242 pages   Price: £8.99

ISBN 1-85249-119-1

Travellers and tourists looking for a traditional British alternative to bland impersonal hotels need look no further than this guide. Contains almost 350 inns which provide Bed and Breakfast as well as excellent real ale.

Guide to Home Brewing

by Graham Wheeler   240 pages   Price: £6.99

ISBN 1-85249-112-4

The definitive beginner's guide to home brewing. The principles, equipment and ingredients are explained and many recipes given.

CAMRA's Best Bottle-Conditioned Beers

CAMRA introduced this award into its *Champion Beer of Britain* contest in 1991.
Judging takes place at the Great British Beer Festival in August each year.

1991

1st	Bass Worthington White Shield
2nd	Guinness Original Stout
3rd	Eldridge Pope Thomas Hardy's Ale

1992

1st	Gale's Prize Old Ale
2nd	Eldridge Pope Thomas Hardy's Ale
3rd	Bass Worthington White Shield

1993

1st	Eldridge Pope Thomas Hardy's Ale
2nd	Courage Imperial Russian Stout

No 3rd place declared.

1994

1st	Courage Imperial Russian Stout
2nd	King & Barnes Festive Ale
3rd	Shepherd Neame Spitfire

1995

1st	King & Barnes Festive Ale
2nd	Gale's Prize Old Ale
3rd	Bass Worthington White Shield

1996

1st	Marston's Oyster Stout
2nd	Bass Worthington White Shield
3rd	Courage Imperial Russian Stout

1997

1st	Hop Back Summer Lightning
2nd	King & Barnes Festive
3rd	Fullers 1845